THE OFFICIAL
F.A. SOCCER
QUIZ BOOK

THE OFFICIAL F.A. SOCCER QUIZ BOOK

More than 1,000 questions
to test your football know-how

ROSTERS LTD

The answers to the quiz questions were correct at the time of going to press.

Published by ROSTERS LTD
23 Welbeck St, London, W1M 7PG

© The Football Association 1990
ISBN 1-85631-008-6

Published in UK by ROSTERS
Typset by Busby The Printers Ltd, Exeter
Printed and bound in Great Britain by Cox and Wyman Ltd, Reading

Acknowledgements
Cover picture and illustrations by Action Images

Also available:

Contents

CHAPTER ONE : PLAYERS

He featured in Manchester United's F.A. Cup-winning team in 1990. Who is he?

1. Which England player is affectionately known to his colleagues as "Digger"?

2. Why was Willie Johnston sent home from Argentina?

3. Who was the first player to be transferred for £1,000?

4. Who was the youngest F.A. Cup finalist?

5. How many League Championship medals has Bryan Robson won?

6. What did "La mano de Dios" do for Diego Maradona?

7. Which German team did Dave Watson briefly play for?

8. What was remarkable about the series of transfers that took Ray Wilkins from Manchester United to Q.P.R.?

9. Who was the "black pearl"?

10. Howard Kendall and Archie Styles moved to Birmingham in 1974 – who moved the other way?

11. Who holds the record for the highest number of goals in a Football League season?

12. Who scored the last hat-trick in an F.A. Cup Final?

13. Who received a serious neck injury as a result of a collision with Harold Schumacher in a World Cup semi-final in 1982?

14. Who scored the quickest goal in a World Cup final tournament?

15. Alfredo Di Stefano played for three countries. Name them.

16. Which former International is an F.A. Council member?

17. Who holds the record number of appearances for Wales?

18. How many times did Billy Wright play for England?

19. Which Sheffield Wednesday player lost a leg following a football injury?

20. Who holds the Celtic club goalscoring record?

21. Who was the last amateur to play for the full England team?

22. Who was the unfortunate Scottish goalkeeper who let in nine English goals in 1961?

23. What record did John Petrie of Arbroath establish in 1885?

24. Who is the oldest player to play in the Football League?

25. What was historic about Bobby Knox's goal for Barrow on 21st August 1965?

26. Who was the first British player to feature in a six-figure transfer?

27. What have Ted Drake, Bill Nicholson, Alf Ramsey, Joe Mercer, Dave Mackay, Bob Paisley and Kenny Dalglish in common?

28. Arnold Birch of Chesterfield scored five Third Division (North) goals in Season 1923-24. So what?

29. What record was Pat Kruse of Torquay United not particularly proud of?

30. What was unusual about the 2-2 draw between Aston Villa and Leicester City in 1976?

31. Arthur Rowley scored four hundred and thirty-four League goals. For which clubs?

32. Jim Smith of Ayr United holds the Scottish League's record for the most goals in a season. How many?

33. Who holds the record for the most goals in a World Cup final tournament?

34. Which West Bromwich Albion manager sold Bryan Robson to Manchester United?

35. Who was 1949 Footballer of the Year and played for both Northern Ireland and the Republic of Ireland?

36. Who scored six goals in an F.A. Cup tie and ended on the losing side?

37. How many English players represented Liverpool in the 1986 F.A. Cup Final?

38. What upset Denis Law about his last League goal?

39. What persuaded Leicester City to sell Gordon Banks to Stoke City?

40. Name England's three goalkeepers in the 1982 World Cup Finals squad.

41. Who scored Liverpool's winner in the 1981 European Cup Final?

42. To which Italian team did Trevor Francis move from Manchester City?

43. Who is the only player/manager to have taken his team to the Football League Championship?

44. Who did Dave Beasant play for between Wimbledon and Chelsea?

45. Name the England coach who played in goal for Wimbledon in the 1963 Amateur Cup Final?

46. Who missed the first F.A. Cup Final penalty at Wembley?

47. Who scored the first F.A. Cup Final penalty at Wembley?

48. Name the Chilean brothers who played for Newcastle shortly after the Second World War.

49. Which England International played professionally in Italy with Napoli and Trani – before joining Crewe Ladies?

50. Who was the first £100-a-week player in the Football League?

51. Who was known as "The Lion of Vienna?"

52. Who is the Guernsey-born striker who has become a leading goalscorer for Southampton?

53. Whose rare headed goal won the 1980 F.A. Cup Final?

54. Three players each scored two goals in the 1989 Simod Cup Final. Name them.

55. Who holds the Walsall all-time League appearance record?

56. Who is Q.P.R.'s most-capped player?

57. Who went to Arsenal for a million, left for a million – and didn't play a match for the club?

58. Who scored the two penalties in the 1974 World Cup Final?

59. Name the Canadian club that Peter Beardsley represented.

60. Which "Green" TV star played in goal for Hereford United?

61. Where was John Barnes born?

62. Name Don Revie's first League club as a player.

63. Which club did Worcestershire's cricket captain play for?

64. Who played in the 1951 F.A. Cup Final as an amateur?

65. Which two brothers both played in goal for Q.P.R. and Sheffield Wednesday?

66. Which England International was born in Singapore?

67. In an alphabetical list of players who have appeared in the Football League, who would come last?

68. Who played for Southend United and Sampdoria?

69. P.F.A. Chief Executive Gordon Taylor only played for teams whose names began with a "B". Can you name them all?

70. Graham Taylor scored only three League goals. With which two clubs?

71. Name West Bromwich Albion's goalkeeper in the 1968 F.A. Cup Final.

72. Who broke his neck in the 1956 F.A. Cup Final?

73. Who scored the first Wembley League Cup Final goal?

74. Which Italian team won the European Cup with three members of the Dutch European Championship winning side of 1988?

75. From which club did John Toshack join Liverpool?

76. What was A.H. Chequer's historic first?

77. Name the Argentinian sent off in the 1966 World Cup quarter-final.

78. Who scored the winning goal in the 1972 League Cup Final?

79. Name the Celtic goalkeeper who died after a match against Rangers in 1931.

80. Who top-scored in the 1970 World Cup Finals?

81. A defender headed England's goalscorers' list in the 1962 World Cup Finals with two penalties. Can you name him?

82. Who was known as "Slim Jim"?

83. Who was the only player in British first class football to maintain a goal-a-game scoring record?

84. Ray Crawford scored two goals to give Fourth Division Colchester United an astonishing win over the mighty Leeds United side in 1971. With which club had Crawford won a League Championship medal?

85. Who played in the F.A. Cup Finals of 1966 and 1976?

86. Who missed the 1983 F.A. Cup Final because of suspension, but was available for the replay?

87. Who became the first player to be sent off in a Wembley F.A. Cup Final?

88. Name the players sent off in the first Wembley F.A. Charity Shield match.

89. Name the Italian club from which Gordon Cowans rejoined Aston Villa.

90. Who scored in both the 1989 and 1990 F.A. Cup semi-finals – but with different clubs?

91. Who moved to Arsenal from Crystal Palace as part of the Clive Allen deal in 1980?

92. What have midfielders Peter Reid, Steve McMahon, Alan Ball and Trevor Steven in common?

93. Who missed the 1986 World Cup because of a broken leg sustained in that year's F.A. Cup semi-finals?

94. What country does John Aldridge represent?

95. Which Yugoslav played right-back for Southampton?

96. Who became the first player born after the 1966 World Cup to win a full England cap?

97. Which player was a member of the England 1982 and 1986 World Cup squads – but didn't get a game in either tournament?

98. Whose injury in Stockholm led F.I.F.A. to worry about A.I.D.S?

99. Who was the young goalkeeper who stood in for Peter Shilton in the 1978 League Cup Final?

100. Who did Bobby Gould gain an F.A. Cup winners' medal with?

CHAPTER TWO :
THE CLUBS

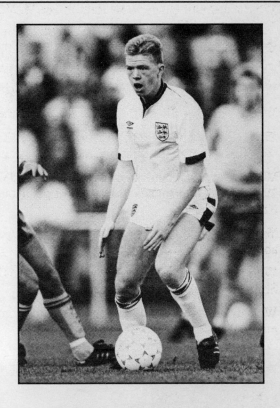

Only one Liverpool player (above) was capped for England at either 'B' or Under-21 level in the 1989-90 season. Who is he?

1. Name the oldest Football League club.

2. Who are "the Imps"?

3. Which club won the last Simod Cup?

4. Which club won the first Football League Cup competition?

5. Which English club was the first to take part in one of the major European competitions?

6. Who plays at Carrow Road?

7. Which was the last club to win the League Championship on goal average?

8. Who plays at The Dell?

9. Keegan, Beardsley and Waddle have all played for the same club. Which one?

10. Which was the first League club to play its home matches on an artificial pitch?

11. Five clubs have won the League Championship on just one occasion. Name them.

12. Who are "the Stags"?

13. Who won the first League Cup Final to be played at Wembley?

14. Which club had three of its players in England's World Cup winning team?

15. Which two League clubs play in the Stoke-on-Trent area?

16. Who are "The Posh"?

17. Which club won the first League Championship to be held after the last war?

18. Which club won the first ever League Championship?

19. With which club did Jimmy Greaves start his League career?

20. Which club missed being one of the League's original members by a single vote?

21. Who plays at Blundell Park?

22. For which club did Ian Rush make his League debut?

23. Who are "the Tigers"?

24. Which club won the F.A. Cup for the first time in their 104th year?

25. Cricketer Ian Botham has played League football for which club?

26. With which club did Mark Lawrenson begin his career as a manager?

27. Which clubs featured in the first League match to be televised live (1983)?

28. Which is the older, Liverpool or Everton?

29. Three clubs have achieved a League Championship hat-trick. Can you name them?

30. Who plays at Griffin Park?

31. Who are "the Pirates"?

32. Which English club did Charlie Nicholas play for?

33. In the 1970s which club had the celebrated midfield trio of Harvey, Kendall and Ball?

34. Denis Law played for both Manchester City and Manchester United. True or false?

35. Which club has scored the most goals in one First Division season?

36. Which club has scored the least goals in one First Division season?

37. Which club has conceded the least number of goals in one First Division season?

38. Who plays at Home Park?

39. Which club did Paul Bracewell leave and subsequently rejoin after several seasons at Everton?

40. Which club was originally called Dial Square?

41. Which club has enjoyed the longest unbeaten sequence in the First Division?

42. Who are "the Hatters"?

43. Who plays at Brisbane Road?

44. Which club has won all four divisional titles?

45. Which two clubs are nicknamed "the Valiants"?

46. Which club was featured in a BBC2 documentary series in 1990?

47. Who are "the Eagles"?

48. What was Swansea City's name before the change in 1970?

49. Only one club has won the F.A. Cup and promotion to the First Division in the same season. Which?

50. How many clubs have won the F.A. Cup and the Football League Cup in the same season?

51. Who is Preston North End's greatest ever goalscorer?

52. Who plays at Bloomfield Road?

53. With which League club do you associate Robert Maxwell?

54. Which club has won the most matches in one First Division season?

55. Which is the second oldest League club?

56. Who plays at St. Andrews?

57. Which club was the first to be automatically promoted into the Football League?

58. Which club was the first to win the Fourth and Third Division Championships in consecutive seasons?

59. Which club has won the League Championship the most times?

60. Which club once won the League Championship without losing a game and the F.A. Cup without conceding a goal in the same season?

61. Which club won the First Division at their first attempt in 1962?

62. John Trollope made seven hundred and seventy League appearances to create a record total for one club. Which one?

63. Who are nicknamed "the Latics"?

64. Whose home is Highbury?

65. Which First Division club has drawn the most matches in one League season?

66. Stockport County have had over thirty managers since the last war. True or false?

67. Only one club has scored and conceded a century of League goals in one season. Which?

68. What colour is Liverpool's change kit?

69. Which club won the F.A. Charity Shield five times in the 1930s?

70. Which club was originally called Small Heath?

71. Who plays at Plough Lane?

72. Which two clubs have their home ground at St. James's Park?

73. Who is Manchester United's most capped player?

74. Which club won the first Zenith Data Systems Cup (1990)?

75. The F.A. Charity Shield fixture has been played at Wembley since 1974. True or false?

76. At which London football ground did Joe Bugner fight Frank Bruno?

77. Walsall once reached the Football League Cup semi-finals. True or false?

78. At which League club did Bobby Moore try his hand as manager?

79. Who is Manchester City's most capped player?

80. What was Chester City's name before 1983?

81. Nottingham Forest have been drawn against both Irish and Scottish clubs in the F.A. Cup. True or false?

82. Who is Leicester City's most capped player?

83. Which club finished runners-up in the Third Division (South) in six consecutive seasons?

84. Who were the visiting side when the first League match on a plastic pitch was played at Loftus Road in 1981?

85. For which club did Terry Butcher make his League debut?

86. Who are "the Owls"?

87. How many times did Newcastle United win the Texaco Cup?

88. Who is Stoke City's most capped player?

89. On whose ground did England play their "away" fixture with Northern Ireland in 1973?

90. Which club was once known as Thames Ironworks?

91. Who won the Mercantile Credit Centenary Trophy?

92. Which was the first League club to be relegated to the GM Vauxhall Conference?

93. Who plays at Prenton Park?

94. For which club did Pat Jennings make more League appearances, Tottenham Hotspur or Arsenal?

95. Which League club do you associate with Elton John?

96. Who are "the Iron"?

97. Who is Liverpool's most capped player?

98. Which club's supporters are "forever blowing bubbles"?

99. Where did Queens Park Rangers play their U.E.F.A. Cup home legs in 1984-85?

100. On whose ground did Henry Cooper fight Cassius Clay?

CHAPTER THREE :
MANAGERS

He played for and managed a World Cup-winning team. Who is he?

1. Who was England's caretaker manager for seven matches in 1974?

2. Name the manager who took both Huddersfield Town and Arsenal to a hat-trick of Championships?

3. Ron Saunders took three different teams to League Cup Finals. Name them.

4. Who was boss at Leeds United for forty-four days?

5. Which former England Amateur International has managed Wimbledon, Watford and Sheffield United?

6. Name the three players who have won Championship medals and gone on to take the same clubs to the title as manager.

7. Who did Harry Catterick manage immediately before joining Everton?

8. Which Scottish team manager died at one of his country's games against Wales?

9. Which physiotherapist became manager of a double-winning side?

10. An international goalkeeper became manager of Juventus. Can you name him?

11. Which academy of soccer produced managers in John Bond, Malcolm Allison and Ken Brown?

12. Name the cigarette-puffing Argentinian who led his country to the World Cup title in 1978.

13. Which European club did he go on to manage?

14. Who said that football wasn't a matter of life and death – it was much more important than that?

15. Bobby Robson and Don Howe played together for

which club?

16. Who was sacked by Manchester United after a much-publicised affair with the wife of the club's physiotherapist?

17. Name two South Americans who managed English Football League clubs in Season 1989-90.

18. Name the actress who plays the fictitious manageress of a football club on TV.

19. What was the result of Sir Alf Ramsey's last match in charge of England?

20. Name Nottingham Forest's manager immediately before Brian Clough.

21. How many F.A. Cup Finals did Liverpool win under Bill Shankly?

22. Which Portuguese club did Keith Burkinshaw manage?

23. Who took Millwall into the First Division?

24. Which League club gave Brian Clough his first managerial job?

25. Who has been the most successful of Liverpool's managers?

26. Among whose clubs have been Bath City, Plymouth Argyle, Manchester City, Crystal Palace and Fisher Athletic?

27. Name the Spanish clubs John Toshack has managed.

28. At Barcelona, Terry Venables had under his charge three British strikers. Can you name them?

29. Name the last manager of the England Amateur Team.

30. How many Championships did Bob Paisley win as manager of Liverpool?

31. Who was manager of Manchester United when they won their last League title?

32. Who was Italy's manager in the 1990 World Cup Finals?

33. Name the German with the Polish name who left Denmark for Turkey!

34. Sir Alf Ramsey briefly managed a Midlands team after leaving the England job. Which?

35. Who is the "bald eagle"?

36. Who did Bobby Robson manage before joining Ipswich Town?

37. Which Irish Republic International managed West Bromwich Albion twice?

38. Who paid the first £1,000,000 transfer fee for an English player moving between English clubs?

39. Which manager brought the European Cup to England for the first time?

40. Who resigned as Coventry City's manager shortly before their first year in Division One?

41. Who managed one British international side while bearing the name of another?

42. Which Northern Ireland International, now a radio personality, was player-manager at Hull City?

43. Which club did Jimmy Seed manage during their golden years in the 1930s?

44. Freddie Goodwin and Willie Bell both played for Leeds United. They also managed the same club. Which?

45. Howard Kendall and Colin Harvey have both managed Everton. What else do they have in common?

46. Who took Southampton into Division One for the first time?

47. Graeme Souness has represented Rangers as player and manager. What other role has he fulfilled for the club?

48. Former Leeds United players Norman Hunter, Allan Clarke and Bobby Collins have all been managers of which other club?

49. Not many people get to manage both Hearts and Hibs. This one also managed Scotland. Who?

50. Q.P.R.'s manager when the Third Division club beat First Division West Bromwich in the 1967 League Cup Final already had one equally notable act of giant-killing under his belt. What was it?

51. And what other major cup feat did he go on to achieve?

52. Did Sir Stanley Matthews ever manage a Football League club?

53. Who was the first to be knighted – Alf Ramsey or Matt Busby?

54. In which year did Liverpool manager Kenny Dalglish join the club as a player?

55. Which Tottenham Hotspur manager brought Argentinian World Cup stars Ardiles and Villa to the club in 1978?

56. Which Dutchman has played for and managed Spanish giants Barcelona?

57. Who brought Steve Daley from Wolves to Manchester City for a fee of £1.4 million in 1979?

58. Which national team manager led his country to first, second and third places in the World Cup and to first and second in the European Championship?

59. Which two Football League clubs has Bobby Charlton managed?

60. Which Spanish club was managed by Howard Kendall?

61. Which manager has been in charge of Ajax, Barcelona, the Dutch national team and Bayer Leverkusen?

62. Which two men formed the managerial partnership that took Coventry City to a Wembley victory in 1987?

63. Who became player-manager of a Third Division club after appearing in eight Championship-winning Liverpool teams?

64. Who was due to succeed Franz Beckenbauer as West Germany's manager after the 1990 World Cup?

65. Just Fontaine of France holds the record for the most goals scored in a World Cup final tournament (13). Did he ever manage the French national team?

66. He represented England at amateur, schoolboy, youth, Under-23 and senior level and now manages a First Division club. Who is he?

67. Who managed the last team to lift the Fairs Cup?

68. He played over six hundred League games for a London club that he now manages. Who is he?

69. Jack Tinn's Portsmouth team were surprise winners of the F.A. Cup in 1939. What was Tinn's trademark?

70. Who captained two F.A. Cup-winning teams in the 1960s and later managed Chelsea?

71. Who was the Sunderland manager who ran onto the field to embrace goalkeeper Montgomery after the F.A. Cup Final of 1973?

72. Who featured in the 1967 and 1982 F.A. Cup Finals, winning as a player in the former and losing as a manager in the latter?

73. Who was the manager, wearing his famous fedora, who took a Third Division club to the F.A. Cup semi-finals in 1976?

74. Who is the only man, post-war, to manage a club which won the championships of the First, Second and Third Divisions?

75. Which four major cups did Tottenham Hotspur win under Bill Nicholson?

76. Under which manager did Wolves win three Championships in the 1950s?

77. Who was Liverpool's manager when they last won the European Champion Clubs' Cup (1984)?

78. Whose team won a Wembley Final on penalty-kicks in 1987?

79. What was the last instance of a former leading scorer in the First Division managing a Football League club?

80. What is the shortest time anyone has served as a manager with a Football League club?

81. Who played under Brian Clough at Nottingham Forest and later managed Hereford United?

82. Who managed both of Bristol's Football League clubs in the 1980s?

83. Who gained an economics degree at Liverpool University, won 42 England caps and became manager of a Second Division club in 1984?

84. Two First Division managers at the start of the 1990-91 season had managed national teams in the past. Who were they?

85. "Nice one, Cyril!" Which Football League clubs has Cyril managed?

86. Which England World Cup captain became player-manager of Stoke City?

87. Who has managed England teams at "B", Under-21, and Semi-Professional levels?

88. Who was Liverpool's manager immediately before Bill Shankly?

89. Can you name West Ham United's six post-war managers?

90. Which one of the following clubs has Tommy Docherty not managed: Aston Villa, Chelsea, Preston North End and Southampton?

91. Which club did George Graham manage prior to taking over at Arsenal?

92. Who succeeded Bobby Robson as Ipswich Town Manager?

93. Who was Watford's manager immediately before Graham Taylor?

94. Who out of the four players to have amassed one hundred caps for England has yet to manage a Football League club?

95. Can you name four England caps who have managed Chelsea since the war?

96. Who was the Derby County's manager before Brian Clough took over?

97. Did Johnny Haynes ever manage Fulham?

98. Who was manager of the England Youth Team when they last won the European Championship (1980)?

99. Which former England goalkeeper managed Canada in the 1986 World Cup?

100. Who has managed both Arsenal and their North London rivals Tottenham Hotspur?

CHAPTER FOUR : NON-LEAGUE

The Sir Thomas Lipton Trophy (above) has been called "the first World Cup". Which English non-League club were its first winners in 1909?

1. Which club achieved the Gola League and F.A. Trophy "double" in 1985?

2. Which England semi-professional cap went on to play for England seniors?

3. Who won the first "Four Nations Tournament" in 1979?

4. What is the record attendance for an F.A. Trophy Final (to the nearest thousand)?

5. Lincoln City needed three matches to beat these F.A. Trophy opponents in 1988. Who were they?

6. Kidderminster won the F.A. Trophy in 1987 but were eliminated by the same club in both 1986 and 1988. Which club was this?

7. Which club won the last F.A. Amateur Cup Final, played in 1974?

8. Who were "Pegasus"?

9. When did a Great Britain team last play in the Olympic football finals?

10. Which club missed a penalty in the last minute of the 1967 F.A. Amateur Cup Final, with the score at 0-0?

11. In which year did the F.A. Trophy Final first go to a replay?

12. In which year was the F.A. Amateur Cup Final first played at Wembley?

13. Who was the England full cap who later played for England semi-pros?

14. Who were the first winners of the F.A. Vase?

15. Who was the ex-England full cap who starred for Matlock in the 1975 F.A. Trophy Final?

16. Which village team from Hampshire reached the F.A. Vase semi-finals in 1988?

17. Who was the ex-Tottenham and Stoke striker who was on target for Tamworth in the 1989 F.A. Vase Final replay?

18. Which Guernsey club drew twice with Brockenhurst in the F.A. Vase in 1987 and won the second replay 9-1?

19. Which was the first ground to be used for an F.A. Vase Final replay?

20. Billericay Town lost only one F.A. Vase tie in four seasons in the 1970s. To whom?

21. Which F.A. Vase-winning team had a Kwiatkowski, a Czarnecki and two Bliszczaks?

22. Which was the last non-League club before Sutton United to beat First Division opposition in the F.A. Cup?

23. Who were the two clubs involved when the GM Vauxhall Conference attendance record was set?

24. Which club once played twenty-one consecutive GM Vauxhall Conference matches at home without defeat?

25. Who was the England semi-professional cap with Northwich who went on to play as a winger for West Ham and Manchester City?

26. Which club was responsible for eight GM Vauxhall Conference clubs' home attendance records (for GMVC matches) being established in Season 1987-88?

27. Which GM Vauxhall Conference club was managed by Tommy Docherty?

28. Which two-time F.A. Trophy winners started life as Rigby Memorial Sunday School F.C.?

29. Which Vauxhall-Opel League club had the honour of playing the full England team prior to the European Championship Finals in 1988?

30. What was the inauspicious start to Chorley's Northern Premier League Championship-winning season?

31. Who were Enfield's F.A. Cup replay opponents when they played at White Hart Lane?

32. Which club defeated Rotherham 4-0 in 1987 for the biggest win by a non-League over Football League opposition in the F.A. Cup for twelve years?

33. Which club failed to complete their GM Vauxhall Conference fixtures in Season 1988-89?

34. Who was the most-capped England Amateur International?

35. Which club won both the F.A. Amateur Cup and the F.A. Trophy within an eight-year period?

36. Which club have been finalists in both the F.A. Amateur Cup and the F.A. Vase?

37. Who were England's opponents in the last Amateur International ever played?

38. The last Olympic football match played in Britain took place in 1971. At which ground?

39. Which Sutton United player so impressed Leeds United in a 1970 Cup tie that they signed him?

40. Which F.A Trophy-winning club once had Gordon Banks as their manager?

41. How many rounds are played in the F.A. Vase competition, including the Final?

42. Which club plays at Wessex Stadium?

43. Who are "the Silkmen"?

44. Yeovil Town were once watched by a crowd of over 80,000. True or false?

45. Where did Croydon play their "home" Cup tie with Millwall in 1979?

46. Where did Weymouth play their "home" league match with Wealdstone in 1988?

47. Which club that started the 1989-90 season in the GM Vauxhall Conference had appeared in two F.A. Vase semi-finals in the 1970s?

48. Which club were three goals up after the first leg of their F.A. Trophy semi-final tie but failed to reach the Final?

49. Which former F.A. Secretary is President of Kingstonian F.C.?

50. Which club that started the 1989-90 season in the Vauxhall League once reached the F.A. Cup semi-finals?

51. Which club moved from the Dolphin to Wexham Park?

52. Who was the goalkeeper who began with Tooting and went on to play in the F.A. Cup Final and also for England?

53. Kerry Dixon once played for the club which lost in the 1968 F.A. Amateur Cup Final. Which club is this?

54. Where did Leatherhead attract a gate of 32,000?

55. Which former F.A. Amateur Cup-winning club could not compete in a league in the 1988-89 season as they had no ground?

56. Which Isthmian League club won 4-0 in a Cup tie against a team managed by Brian Clough?

57. Have Wembley ever got to Wembley?

58. Which is the nearest F.A. Vase club to Epsom Racecourse?

59. Which club that started the 1989-90 season in the Vauxhall League was once managed by Ron Greenwood?

60. Who went from Hayes to West Bromwich Albion and then onto an F.A. Cup-winners' medal with Coventry?

61. Which Vauxhall League club had only been formed in 1985?

62. Which island club plays in the Essex Senior League?

63. Which club moved from the Spartan League to the Sussex County League in 1988?

64. Which club during the 1980s competed in the Sussex County, Wessex and Combined Counties Leagues?

65. Which Southern League club played in the European Cup Winners' Cup in 1987?

66. With which league was the Westgate Insurance Cup associated?

67. Which non-League clubs share their ground with League clubs?

68. Which Southern League club had Dominic Genovese and Mario Ippolitto in attack?

69. From which non-League club did Trevor Senior join Portsmouth?

70. Which club moved from Bath Lane to Cams Alders?

71. The 1982 F.A. Vase winners have since changed their name. To what?

72. Who are "The Yeltz"?

73. Which goalkeeper did Brian Clough buy from Gravesend & Northfleet?

74. Which club used to be "Thanet United"?

75. Which club won four consecutive Western League titles in the 1970s?

76. Which club won four consecutive West Midlands League titles in the 1980s?

77. Which F.A. Amateur Cup finalists of the 1960s had three seasons in the Hellenic League in the 1980s?

78. How many Bournemouth clubs play in the F.A. Cup?

79. Who scored for Barrow in under four seconds?

80. Which non-League club sold Tony Galvin to Tottenham?

81. What do Hyde United and Feltham both have?

82. Which Buckinghamshire club had a Trinidad International?

83. Two top Merseyside non-Leaguers, Marine and South Liverpool, both had their home attendance records set against the same opposition. Who was that?

84. Which two players moved from South Liverpool to Liverpool F.C. and scored in the F.A. Cup Final?

85. Who are the two senior non-League clubs in Northwich?

86. Which are the three "Sutton" clubs in F.A. competitions?

87. Which was the first club to win the North-West Counties League Cup twice?

88. Which F.A. Vase club in the Sheffield area was formed in 1860?

89. Which club were founder members of the Northern League, winning nineteen league titles and ten F.A. Amateur Cup finals?

90. Which was the only Vauxhall-Opel League club to reach one hundred points in Season 1988-89?

91. Who were the last ever Athenian League champions?

92. What is the record attendance for an F.A. Vase Final (to the nearest thousand)?

93. Who were the opponents when a Blyth Spartans "home" match attracted a crowd of 42,000?

94. In the 1964-65 F.A. Amateur Cup competition one club won their First Round match 10-0 and their Second Round match 11-2. Who was this?

95. The England Amateur Team played five Internationals on a European tour in 1973. How many goals were conceded in total?

96. Which Isle of Man club competes in the F.A. Vase?

97. Which English non-League club found itself playing

against a team that included Brazilian World Cup stars Socrates and Rivelino?

98. In which league could you see National Westminster Bank play Crouch End Vampires?

99. In which league could you see Tenisonians play Uffingtonians?

100. One player scored the winning goal in the F.A. Vase Final in 1983 and the F.A. Trophy Final in 1989. Who?

CHAPTER FIVE :
F.A. CUP

Two rival managers before an F.A. Cup Final in the 1980s. Whose team won?

1. In what year was the Final first played at Wembley?

2. What happened to the original F.A. Cup trophy?

3. Has a team from outside England ever won the Cup?

4. Who was the first player to miss a penalty in a Wembley Final?

5. Which was the last non-League club to win the Cup?

6. Have Irish clubs ever played in the Cup?

7. Which were the two non-League teams to beat First Division opposition in the 1980s?

8. What was "the Wembley hoodoo"?

9. Who was the youngest player to have appeared in a Final?

10. What Cup record is held by The Hon. Sir Arthur Fitzgerald Kinnaird, Kt.?

11. Who played in the Finals of 1937 and 1938 and managed the Cup-winning teams in 1965 and 1974?

12. Has there ever been a Final between two Second Division teams?

13. Who was the Argentinian who scored twice in the 1981 Final replay?

14. How many clubs took part in the very first Cup competition?

15. Which club got to a Wembley Final despite losing in an earlier round?

16. What was unusual about Preston's goalkeeper in the 1922 Final?

17. Who scored nine goals in a First Round match in 1971?

18. When the Luton v Manchester City match was abandoned in 1961, one City player had netted six times. Who was that?

19. An F.A. Cup semi-final tie was once played at an Edinburgh castle. True or false?

20. Which Cup tie lasted for eleven hours?

21. Which non-League club held Manchester United to a draw at Old Trafford in the 1950s?

22. How many different grounds have been used for the Final?

23. How many different grounds have been used for a Final replay?

24. Has Bobby Robson ever managed a Cup-winning team?

25. Which was the first Wembley Final to end in a draw?

26. Which club won the very first Final?

27. Who was the last amateur player to appear in a Final?

28. Which recent Cup-winning team had only joined the Football League in 1977?

29. Which one of these players has scored the winning goal in a Final: Clive Allen, Trevor Brooking or George Best?

30. When did the ball burst in the Final?

31. Who won F.A. Cup-winners' medals for Tottenham and a Scottish F.A. Cup-winners' medal for Hearts?

32. Why do the Cup-winners come back to Wembley three months later?

33. Which famous old club once had a rule never to enter for competitions and then made an impact in the Cup in the 1920s?

34. Who is the youngest player to score in a Final?

35. Who is the youngest captain in a Final?

36. A Third Round match once had an official attendance of nil. True or false?

37. In which year did the famous "Graf-Zeppelin" airship fly over Wembley while the Final was in progress?

38. In which year did a Cup Final crowd first reach six figures?

39. One club featured in five Finals inside seven years at the old Crystal Palace ground and failed to win any of them. Which club?

40. In which year was the "Khaki Final" played?

41. What has been the biggest margin of victory in a Final?

42. Has the Final ever gone to two replays?

43. The Cup competition once had a thousand entries. True or false?

44. When was the Final last played in April?

45. Who won the Cup in 1919?

46. Did the famous goalscorer "Dixie" Dean ever score in a Final?

47. Which player scored in the Finals of 1953 and 1958?

48. The last time Nottingham Forest won the Cup, the Final was refereed by Mr. Clough. True or false?

49. Which are the three clubs to have achieved a post-war "double"?

50. How many post-war Finals have ended in a draw?

51. Which non-League club reached the Third Round three times in four years in the 1960s?

52. Which non-League club won through to the Third Round in 1964 and were drawn against the previous season's losing finalists?

53. The highest recorded attendance at Tottenham Hotspur's ground watched a Sixth Round tie in 1938 (75,038). Who were Spurs' opponents then?

54. What is the highest number of Cup-winners' medals won by an individual player?

55. What Cup record is held by Andy Awford of Worcester City?

56. How much did the present Cup trophy cost?

57. Which club won the 100th Final?

58. Which non-League club won at First Division Burnley in the Third Round in 1975 and then held Leeds United to a draw at Elland Road in the Fourth?

59. How many rounds has the competition had in recent years, including the Final?

60. In which year was the hymn "Abide With Me" first sung at the Final?

61. Why was the competition called the "Challenge Cup"?

62. A team from Chatham has played in the Final. True or false?

63. Why was there no possibility of the referee awarding a penalty in the first Final?

64. Which club's players received two medals each for playing in the Final?

65. Which goalkeeper played in three consecutive Finals, starting in 1978?

66. Which club won the Cup and then didn't lose another tie for seven seasons?

67. In which year did the reigning monarch first attend the Final?

68. Who was the Devonshire fisherman who won three winners' medals with Bolton Wanderers in the 1920s?

69. Did Bill Shankly ever play in the Final?

70. Which Final team weren't helped by monkey glands?

71. What do Bert Turner (Charlton) and Tommy Hutchison (Coventry) have in common?

72. When Charlton Athletic met Derby County in the 1946 Final, it was Charlton's third Wembley final in four years. True or false?

73. In which year did two London clubs first contest a Wembley Cup Final?

74. How much were Aston Villa, the holders, fined by the F.A. after the Cup was stolen?

75. In which year was the rule introduced whereby extra time was to be played if the teams were all square after ninety minutes in the Final?

76. Where was the first Final replay staged?

77. "Wanderers" were the first winners of the Cup. Was there any connection between that club and the present "Wolverhampton Wanderers"?

78. Which was the first Fourth Division club to reach the Sixth Round?

79. Sheffield Wednesday missed one year's Cup competition because they were too late with their entry. True or false?

80. Which was the first Second Divison club to lift the Cup?

81. What was unique about Manchester United's progress to the 1948 Final?

82. In one of the greatest "giant-killings" in Cup history, Yeovil Town defeated First Division Sunderland 2-1 in 1949. But who beat them 8-0 in the next round?

83. Who played in the first Wembley final for Bolton Wanderers and managed Blackpool to victory in the "Matthews Final" thirty years later?

84. Who played in five Wembley finals between the wars?

85. Bolton Wanderers' team to win the Cup in 1926 was unchanged from that which had lifted the same trophy three years earlier. True or false?

86. Which was the first club to win the Cup with an all-English side?

87. Which was the first Third Division club, post-war, to reach the Cup semi-finals?

88. Since the inaugural F.A. Charity Shield match was staged in 1908, the F.A. Cup winners have always taken part. True or false?

89. Lillie Bridge was the ground used for the second Final in 1873. Where was Lillie Bridge?

90. In which year did the gate receipts at the Final first exceed £100,000?

91. Who was the only Tottenham Hotspur player to appear in all of the club's three Cup Finals in the 1960s?

92. Five consecutive Cup Finals in the 1970s finished with only one of the two competing teams scoring. Which player ended the sequence by netting an equaliser in the following year's match?

93. Tottenham Hotspur won fourteen ties in a row during a period in the early 1980s when they won the Cup twice. Which club finally beat them?

94. In which year was a semi-final last staged at Highbury?

95. Who missed the 1986 World Cup in Mexico as a result of an injury received in a Cup semi-final at White Hart Lane?

96. Why did Liverpool feel more confident of success in the 1986 Final after Ian Rush had equalised Gary Lineker's opener for Everton?

97. Wimbledon's F.A. Cup triumph came twenty-five years after they had won the F.A. Amateur Cup. Which club had they beaten at Wembley in 1963?

98. How many Finals have there been?

99. Did Matthews score in the "Matthews Final"?

100. What is taken to Wembley on Cup Final day every year but is never used?

CHAPTER SIX :
ENGLAND

Peter Shilton received a silver salver to mark his 100th
England appearance. Who were England's opponents
at that match?

1. England's youngest post-war player was Duncan Edwards. How old was he when he made his England debut?

2 Who was the last amateur to play for the full England team?

3. Who played in seventy consecutive England Internationals between 1951 and 1959?

4. Who was the first professional to appear for England while on the books of a club outside the Football League?

5. Why was England's World Cup quarter-final with Argentina in 1966 held up for seven minutes in the first half?

6. Which was the first country outside the United Kingdom to defeat England at home?

7. Can you name two England Managers who have played in the World Cup Finals?

8. Who was England's caretaker manager for seven matches in 1974?

9. What is the record attendance for an England home match?

10. Who were England's opponents at the first "all seater" Wembley match?

11. Which country did England beat 17-0 in 1951?

12. Who was the first player to reach one hundred caps for England?

13. Who set a new England caps record in his last International?

14. Who was the Arsenal outside-left and Middlesex batsman who represented England at both football and cricket?

15. Can you name two brothers who played together for England as professionals?

16. Can you name a father and son who have both played for England?

17. In what year were the floodlights first switched on during an England match at Wembley?

18. The England team is administered by The Football Association. Where are the F.A.'s headquarters?

19. England beat Cyprus 5-0 in a European Championship qualifier at Wembley in 1975 and one player scored all five goals. Who was that?

20. Which player has scored the most goals in his career as an England International?

21. Which club supplied no fewer than seven of the players who represented England against Italy at Highbury in 1934?

22. England's first defeat abroad was against Spain in 1929. What was the score?

23. Who were England's first international opponents?

24. International football owes its beginning to the enterprise of the F.A. Secretary in 1870. What was his name?

25. The first official international match between England and a foreign country was played in 1908. Who were England's opponents then?

26. Who were England playing when they achieved their 100th Wembley victory?

27. Who was the 1,000th player to win a full England cap?

28. Who made his England debut in 1934 and was still playing in the First Division when he was fifty years old?

29. Who has been England's youngest captain?

30. What shirt number was Geoff Hurst wearing when he netted a World Cup Final hat-trick in 1966?

31. Who was the first England player to be sent off in a Full International?

32. How many goals has the great Pelé scored against England?

33. When did England first play in the World Cup Finals?

34. How many World Cup semi-final ties have England played in?

35. Who was the first England substitute to score?

36. Who were England's first Wembley opponents in 1924?

37. Who were the "Wembley Wizards" who trounced England 5-1 at Wembley in 1928?

38. Who grabbed a hat-trick as England beat Luxembourg 9-0 in a European Championship qualifier at Wembley in 1982? Clue: He later played in Italy for AC Milan.

39. His father played in goal for Ipswich Town. He himself was England's goalkeeper on two occasions in 1985. Who is he?

40. Gordon Banks was forced to miss the World Cup quarter-final match with West Germany in 1970 through illness. Who stepped in to take his place?

41. Who came on as a substitute at Hampden Park in 1989 and scored on his England debut?

42. Whose white England shirt was almost red after the World Cup qualifier in Stockholm in 1989?

43. Who came on as an England substitute during a Wembley match in 1985, and laid on Gary Lineker's winning goal, but has not played for England since then? (That was his one and only appearance.)

44. England's match in Iceland in 1982 was upgraded to a "Full International" and two players thereby won their only cap. Who were they?

45. Mark Hateley headed one of two goals that sunk the Brazilians in Rio in 1984. Which club was he with at that time?

46. When was an England match at Wembley last cancelled because of the weather?

47. He scored on his England debut against Bulgaria in 1979, went on to win over fifty caps and play in the French League. Who is he?

48. Kevin Keegan's first three Internationals were all against the same country. Which one?

49. Who won the "Golden Boot" for his World Cup scoring exploits in Mexico?

50. He replaced Mick Channon as a late substitute against Wales at Wembley in 1975 for his only England cap and managed a GM Vauxhall Conference club in Season 1989-90. Who is he?

51. Who was the "Lion of Vienna"?

52. Who won his fiftieth and last England cap by virtue of coming on as a substitute for the last few seconds against France in Bilbao?

53. Who was England's captain for the 1982 World Cup Finals?

54. Which England World Cup winner was said by his manager to be "ten years ahead of his time"?

55. What shirt number did Bryan Robson wear on his England debut?

56. How many caps did Bobby Robson win as a player?

57. Which England goalkeeper later managed the Canadian national team?

58. Which of these South American countries has yet to play at Wembley: Chile, Paraguay, Colombia?

59. England has met this country in seventeen Internationals, but they have not been to Wembley since 1964. Which country is this?

60. Which were the three countries in England's first round group in the 1966 World Cup Finals?

61. England took part in the U.S. Bicentennial Tournament in 1976 with three other teams. Who were they?

62. What colours did England wear against Czechoslovakia in Guadalajara?

63. Which was Bobby Robson's first match in charge?

64. In which year did Peter Shilton make his England debut?

65. Which Haitian embarrassed England in Belo Horizonte?

66. Are these players all England caps: Nigel Spink, Mark Barham, Nick Pickering?

67. England's first twelve matches against this country produced twelve victories and seventy-nine goals for England. Which country was this?

68. Which was the first England match at Wembley to generate more than £1 million in gate receipts?

69. When England drew their World Cup qualifier with Poland in 1973, thereby failing to make the Finals, which England striker came on as a substitute with ninety seconds remaining?

70. Who was England's first World Cup substitute?

71. One England match at Wembley was so one-sided that Gordon Banks could only remember touching the ball four times, all from back-passes. Who were England's opponents that evening?

72. When did Northern Ireland last win at Wembley?

73. England has only met this country once and the match finished goalless. Which country is this?

74. Who was the only other England player, apart from Gary Lineker, to score in the 1986 World Cup Finals?

75. Which country has played against England five times but never in England?

76. When did England achieve a 9-3 victory over Scotland at Wembley?

77. What is thought to be the fastest post-war England goal?

78. Who scored all four goals when England won 4-2 in Madrid in 1987?

79. England qualified for the 1990 World Cup Finals without conceding a single goal. Which was the only other country in the world to achieve such a feat?

80. Which was the last country in the 1980s to beat England at Wembley?

81. Who scored the last Wembley goal of the 1980s?

82. Which three countries did England meet on their 1984 South American tour?

83. Has an England team ever played in the Olympics?

84. Which England wing-half scored in four consecutive Internationals in the 1960s?

85. Who is the only England Manager to have been knighted while in the job?

86. In a match to mark the Centenary of the F.A., England beat the Rest of the World 2-1 at Wembley in 1963. Can you name either of the England scorers?

87. Who scored on his England debut in Egypt in 1986 but has not been capped since?

88. Which striker won six England caps in the 1970s and managed a team that got to Wembley in 1990?

89. A protégé of Malcolm Allison at Crystal Palace, he made his England debut when still a Third Division player. Who was he?

90. In how many World Cups have England taken part?

91. Who were the first winners of the Rous Cup?

92. Which country beat England 6-3 and 7-1 within seven months in the 1950s?

93. Who was the West Ham goalkeeper who made his only England appearance in Sir Alf Ramsey's last match in charge?

94. Where did England play their last International in England that was not at Wembley?

95. Five months before England defeated West Germany in the World Cup Final they had played them in a Wembley Friendly. What was the score?

96. Gary Lineker injured a wrist ten days before the 1986 World Cup Finals began and had it bandaged throughout the tournament. In which match had he received the injury?

97. Who scored sixty goals in one First Division season and three hundred and seventy-nine in all in his League career but won less than twenty England caps?

98. When did England last play an International in December?

99. Which English player holds the record for the most goals scored in the British Championship?

100. Two England players, Terry Butcher and John Barnes, were actually born outside England. Where?

CHAPTER SEVEN : EUROPEAN FOOTBALL

Sometimes called "the European Pele." Who is this?

1. Who were the first winners of the European Champion Clubs' Cup?

2. How many times have Liverpool won the Champions' Cup?

3. Which Italian club is often referred to as "The Old Lady"?

4. Who has played the most Internationals for the Republic of Ireland?

5. Which was the first English club to win the Champions' Cup?

6. Which was the first English club to win the European Cup Winners' Cup?

7. Who were the first winners of the European Nations Cup?

8. Which club was the first to win all three European club competitions?

9. How many times have Liverpool won the U.E.F.A. Cup?

10. Which French club did Ray Wilkins once briefly play for?

11. Which was the first English club to win the European Super Cup?

12. Which club plays at the "Stadium of Light"?

13. Maradona left this club and Terry Venables joined them. Which club?

14. What is Real Madrid's "reserve team" called?

15. Who did Bobby Robson succeed as coach at PSV Eindhoven?

16. Mulhouse is a club in which country?

17. Which two Spanish clubs has John Toshack managed?

18. Which Spanish club did Jock Wallace once manage?

19. Which two continental clubs did Mark Hughes play for before his second spell at Manchester United?

20. In which Italian city is the Lazio club based?

21. Who won the first Champions' Cup Final to be decided on penalty-kicks?

22. Has the European Championship title ever been decided in a shoot-out?

23. Which Italian club did Luther Blissett join from Watford?

24. Who refereed the first Champions' Cup Final in 1956?

25. For which Football League club did the Dutchman Hans Van Breukelen keep goal?

26. John Aldridge and Kevin Richardson are connected with which Spanish club?

27. From which other Italian club did Juventus sign Roberto Baggio for a world record transfer fee in 1990?

28. Which prolific goalscorer in Spain is known as "The Vulture"?

29. In which stadium did Real Madrid record their memorable 7-3 defeat of Eintracht Frankfurt in the Champions' Cup Final?

30. Which was the first English club to take part in the Champions' Cup?

31. Who are the Italian giants largely funded by Fiat?

32. Did Leeds United reach a Champions' Cup Final under Revie?

33. A Scottish club won the Champions' Cup before an English one did. True or false?

34. Who did Bobby Robson's Ipswich defeat in the U.E.F.A. Cup Final?

35. Which Northern Ireland club has appeared in the Champions' Cup the most times?

36. Which English club has appeared in the Cup Winners' Cup the most times?

37. Who do Maradona and Mars have in common?

38. "17 Nentori" are a top club in which country?

39. Has a "London" team ever played in a European club competition?

40. What is Real Madrid's home ground called?

41. Who was the first "European Player of the Year"?

42. Clive Allen once played for which French club?

43. If you were watching a League match between Beveren and Beerschot, what country would you be in?

44. Celtic striker Dziekanowski has won caps for Yugoslavia. True or false?

45. Which two top club sides did Paul Breitner play for?

46. Who captained Manchester United to victory and scored twice in the 1968 Champions' Cup Final?

47. Which two English clubs have appeared in the U.E.F.A. Cup on the most occasions?

48. In which city was an English club last victorious in a European final?

49. How many times was Dutch legend Johan Cruyff voted "European Player of the Year"?

50. Which Spanish club did Adrian Heath briefly play for?

51. Who was the first Soviet player to appear for a Football League club?

52. From which Italian club did Celtic sign Paul Elliott?

53. Luigi Riva helped a Sardinian club to the "Serie A" Championship in 1970. Which club was this?

54. If you were watching a League match featuring Valladolid and Oviedo, in which country would you be?

55. Which Italian club did Jimmy Greaves play for?

56. Which club were Leeds United trying to emulate when changing their playing strip to "all white"?

57. Which English club were Juventus copying when they decided on black and white striped shirts?

58. Which French club did Maurice Johnston leave to link up with Rangers?

59. Which country will stage the European Championship Finals in 1992?

60. Chris Waddle left Tottenham to join which French club?

61. Who were the three Internazionale players who won the 1990 World Cup with West Germany?

62. Which Spanish club did Ron Atkinson manage?

63. Which club won the first World Club Championship?

64. Who refereed the first European Nations Cup Final?

65. What was the unusual aggregate score when Chelsea met Jeunesse Hautcharage of Luxembourg in the Cup Winners' Cup?

66. In which year did Ian Rush win the "Golden Boot"?

67. Who holds the record for the most goals scored for an English club in European competitions?

68. What is England's best performance to date in the European Championship?

69. What is the record attendance at a Champions' Cup Final?

70. Which two Dutch players did Bobby Robson sign for Ipswich Town in the 1970s?

71. In which country was Welsh cap Pat Van Den Hauwe born?

72. League matches in Denmark are never played in December. True or false?

73. What competition must a European club win in order to qualify for the Toyota Cup?

74. Ferencvaros and Videoton are clubs from which country?

75. Whose home ground is Nou Camp?

76. Which Finnish club, who are regulars in European competition, are based close to the Arctic Circle?

77. Has the destiny of the Cup Winners' Cup trophy ever been decided over two legs?

78. Fearing fixture congestion, the Football League advised which club not to take part in the inaugural Champions' Cup?

79. Manchester City's last goal in European competition was scored by a Pole. True or false?

80. Who was the million pound player whose goal won the Champions' Cup for Brian Clough?

81. Who was the surprise scorer of three goals in Newcastle United's 6-2 victory over Ujpest Dozsa in the Fairs Cup Final?

82. Which two English clubs were allowed back into European competition for the 1990-91 season?

83. Which was the first club in Denmark to turn professional?

84. Which two teams played their first ever European Championship fixtures in 1990?

85. What colours did Manchester United wear in their European final?

86. Which club from the Beazer Homes League won their home leg against Atalanta in the Cup Winners' Cup?

87. Who scored the goals when West Ham United last won a European final?

88. Only one Greek club has reached a European final. Which?

89. By which name are the crack Yugoslav club "Crvena Zvezda" better known in Britain?

90. Which Italian club signed Zico in 1983?

91. In 1990 the winners of the three European club competitions came from the same country. Which country?

92. Aberdeen's Cup Winners' Cup triumph in 1983 was achieved against which famous club?

93. Which was the first Welsh club to compete in Europe?

94. Which of the three major European finals is played over two legs?

95. Which West German club signed Kevin Keegan in 1977?

96. Which top Dutch club receives financial backing from Philips?

97. Many German clubs have the word ''Eintracht'' included in their name. What does this mean in English?

98. On their way to lifting the Champions' Cup for the first time Liverpool were seconds away from losing on aggregate to St. Etienne in the quarter-finals. Who popped up to score the decisive goal?

99. Defender Paolo Maldini was a star of Italy's World Cup team in 1990. Is it true that his father once played in a Wembley Cup Final?

100. Which competition is thought to have been the forerunner of all European club tournaments?

CHAPTER EIGHT : WORLD CUP

World Cup-winning manager Alf Ramsey in conversation with two players during an England training session. Who is the player on his immediate right in the picture?

1. U.S.A. once reached the World Cup semi-finals. True or false?

2. Who was the top scorer in the 1970 World Cup in Mexico?

3. Which country hosted the first World Cup?

4. Name the Chilean goalkeeper who feigned injury in a qualifying match against Brazil in 1989.

5. Which is the only country to have appeared in all fourteen Finals?

6. Who captained the World Cup-winning Argentinian team in 1978?

7. Who successfully managed the Italian team in 1982?

8. In the 1982 Finals which two countries avoided defeat but were still eliminated?

9. Which country was the first to win the World Cup on foreign soil?

10. In the history of the competition only one country has declined to defend its title. Which?

11. Which was the first World Cup at which substitutes were allowed?

12. Which two countries have staged two final tournaments?

13. In the 1966 Final Geoff Hurst scored a hat-trick. Who contributed England's other goal?

14. Who netted England's first goal in the 1990 Finals?

15. For which Finals did Scotland last fail to qualify?

16. In which year did U.S.A. sensationally beat England 1-0?

17. When Gordon Banks fell ill in Mexico in 1970, who replaced him as England's goalkeeper?

18. Who was the top scorer in the 1986 Finals?

19. Who scored the winning spot-kick for the Republic of Ireland in their penalty shoot-out with Romania in 1990?

20. Who was sent off against England in the 1966 quarter-final at Wembley?

21. How many goals did Gordon Banks concede in England's six matches in the 1966 Finals?

22. In which Finals did all four British countries compete?

23. Who missed with a penalty-kick in the 1982 Final?

24. In which country will the 1994 Finals be held?

25. Which country was the first to win the World Cup three times?

26. Who scored both of England's goals in the 1966 semi-final with Portugal?

27. In which year did Brazil first win the trophy?

28. Which was the second country to win the trophy three times?

29. Who was the top scorer in the 1978 Finals?

30. How many goals did Pele score in the Finals?

31. Who were England's two reserve goalkeepers in 1966?

32. Who was England's manager in Mexico in 1986?

33. Who said: "They think it's all over . . . it is now!"?

34. Did George Best ever play in the Finals?

35. Who has scored the most goals in final tournaments?

36. After whom was the first World Cup trophy named?

37. Name the four European countries which took part in 1930?

38. Which has been the only country to score ten goals in a World Cup Finals match, excluding shoot-outs?

39. How many times has the Final ended with a 1-0 scoreline?

40. Who presented the trophy to Bobby Moore in 1966?

41. Who captained the 1990 winners?

42. In which Finals did U.S.S.R. first compete?

43. Apart from Wembley (which, strictly speaking, is in Middlesex), which other London ground was used in 1966?

44. How many Argentinian players were suspended from the 1990 Final?

45. Who captained England in the 1982 Finals?

46. Argentina were victors in 1978 – but which country had beaten them in a group match?

47. Who registered U.S.A.'s goal in their famous win against England?

48. Have Scotland ever progressed to the quarter-finals?

49. Whose late equaliser took the 1966 Final into extra time?

50. Which team won the "Fair Play" award in 1990?

51. West Germany won the 1974 Final after only finishing second in their group. Which country topped the group?

52. Who was the first player to be sent off in a Final?

53. Who was the Mexican goalkeeper who played in five tournaments?

54. Who scored the first ever World Cup goal?

55. Who designed the present World Cup trophy?

56. How many different countries have won the World Cup?

57. Who was top scorer in the 1990 Finals?

58. How many goals were credited to Roger Milla of Cameroon in the 1990 Finals?

59. Who managed Scotland in the Mexico Finals of 1986?

60. When did England last miss the Finals?

61. Which two players failed with spot-kicks against West Germany in the 1990 semi-final shoot-out?

62. Against which country did Peter Shilton establish a new world record of 120 international caps?

63. Who was top scorer in the 1966 Finals?

64. Who was the Brazilian who scored in each of his country's six matches in 1970?

65. Who was captain of the winning Argentinian team in 1986?

66. How many times has an Englishman refereed the Final?

67. Who managed Scotland in the 1978 Finals?

68. Who scored the goal that won the World Cup in 1990?

69. Both Diego Maradona and Johan Cruyff have been cautioned in the Final. True or false?

70. How many yellow cards were shown to Paul Gascoigne in Italia '90?

71. Who netted for Cameroon to get Italia '90 off to a surprising start with their victory against Argentina, the holders?

72. Who was the English referee who officiated at Italia '90?

73. Four players in England's 1990 squad did not actually play. How many can you name?

74. Who has been the oldest scorer in the Finals?

75. Which country did Ivica Osim manage in 1990?

76. Who finished third in 1966?

77. Who finished third in 1990?

78. How many goals did the Republic of Ireland score in Italia '90, excluding shoot-outs?

79. What was Paul Gascoigne's shirt number in the Finals?

80. Which African country found themselves at the wrong end of a 9-0 scoreline in 1974?

81. Which two countries are already qualified for the 1994 Finals?

82. Which England star announced his retirement from international football after the 1990 World Cup?

83. Who managed Northern Ireland in the 1986 Finals?

84. Who was the last player to notch four goals in one Finals match?

85. In the 1978 Final, with the score at 1-1 and only seconds remaining, which player had just the goal-keeper to beat to win the Cup for Holland but hit the post?

86. Who captained Brazil to ultimate success in 1970?

87. Only one manager has led his country to two World Cup triumphs. Who?

88. England had three captains during the 1990 tournament. Can you name them?

89. At which airport did England receive an enthusiastic welcome when returning home from the 1990 Finals?

90. Has a player ever captained two World Cup-winning sides?

91. Who wore the No. 2 shirt for Argentina in 1978?

92. Who wore the No. 1 shirt for Argentina in 1982?

93. Who was the oldest player in the 1990 Finals?

94. Has a player ever twice been top scorer in the World Cup?

95. Which two countries qualified automatically for the 1966 World Cup?

96. What was the 1990 World Cup mascot called?

97. What was England's 1990 World Cup song entitled?

98. When did ''World Cup Willie'' reign supreme?

99. When were the England players singing ''Back Home''?

100. Over five goals per match were scored at the 1954 Finals in Switzerland. True or false?

CHAPTER NINE : LAWS OF THE GAME

Who is this? He was the only English referee at the 1990 World Cup.

1. A player is sent off in the kick-about before the kick-off. The referee refuses to allow a substitute to replace him. Is he right?

2. What do continental footballers mean by "an eleven-metre kick"?

3. What choice does the captain have if he wins the toss?

4. A match is in progress on a ground with no flood-lights. The referee does not think the match can be completed in daylight unless the teams change straight round at half-time. One player insists on a five-minute break. Can the referee order that the interval is not taken?

5. The attacking side is awarded a free-kick for dangerous play by a defender. A forward takes the kick; the ball strikes the referee and deflects into the goal. What is the referee's decision?

6. The referee awards a penalty. Before the kick can be taken, he decides that the ninety minutes are up. Does he blow for time?

7. Can the goalkeeper take a throw-in?

8. Can a team choose to play without a goalkeeper?

9. A defender, standing on the line marking the edge of the penalty area, trips an attacker. Is it a penalty?

10. What is a place-kick?

11. An indirect free-kick is awarded to the attacking team, six yards from goal. Where can the defenders stand?

12. Does the referee have to wear black?

13. The goalkeeper moves his feet before a penalty is taken. The ball goes into the goal. Should the referee order the kick to be retaken?

14. What is the penalty for a foul throw?

15. Can the referee send a player off for dissent?

16. Do players have to wear boots?

17. In what circumstances can a referee allow a player who has been sent off to come back onto the field?

18. The referee stops the game to send a player off for foul language. How does he restart the game?

19. What colour cards indicate: (a) a caution, (b) a sending off?

20. The ball is rolling into the goal, when a dog runs onto the pitch and stops it. Can the referee award a goal?

21. A player takes a penalty and hits the bar. The ball rebounds straight to the kicker who shoots into the goal. Is it a goal?

22. What was the big change in the offside law of 1925?

23. Who decides the laws of the game?

24. The referee finds his watch has stopped and that he has accidently played fifty minutes in the first half. Can he decide to play only forty minutes in the second half to compensate?

25. Is a player allowed to pull an opponent out of the way if he is being obstructed?

26. How many steps can a goalkeeper take with the ball after he has controlled it with his hands?

27. If a player (not the goalkeeper) controls the ball with his upper arm, does this count as "hands"?

28. How wide is the penalty area from side to side?

29. Can the referee send off a linesman?

30. What is the penalty against a goalkeeper who handles the ball outside his own penalty area?

31. What is the purpose of the arc drawn on the edge of the penalty area?

32. What is the permitted circumference of the ball?

33. Can an opposing player head the ball out of the hands of the goalkeeper?

34. What, according to the laws, should a referee do if a player: (a) leaves the field without permission, then (b) comes back on again without permission?

35. Who invented the diagonal system of refereeing?

36. What are the dimensions of the goals?

37. Do you measure the width of the goals: (a) from centre of goal-post to centre of goal-post, (b) from outside of goal-post to outside of goal-post or (c) from inside of goal-post to inside of goal-post?

38. Are the flags on the half-way line necessary?

39. Can a referee order a player to remove a wedding ring?

40. Can a goal be scored direct from the kick-off?

41. A player taking a free-kick rolls the ball six inches sideways to a colleague who hits it, while it is still moving, into the goal. Should a goal be allowed?

42. What is the minimum height of the corner flag?

43. A goalkeeper is fouled right on his own goal-line. He complains to the referee that he does not have room to take the kick. The referee makes him take the kick from where the offence occurred. Is he right?

44. How many law are there?

45. Which law deals with offside?

46. Can a player be offside in his own half?

47. Can a player be offside from a throw-in?

48. Can a pitch be square?

49. What is the maximum length of the pitch for inter-national matches?

50. What is the maximum number of substitutions allowed per team in a competition match?

51. There are nine offences which are penalised by a direct free-kick. How many can you name?

52. A defender is awarded a direct free-kick. He plays the ball back to his goalkeeper, who isn't looking! The ball goes straight into the goal. Is this a goal?

53. For how long is the goalkeeper allowed to hold onto the ball?

54. What does a player's equipment consist of?

55. How far away should the players of the defending side be at a free-kick?

56. Can a player take a throw-in using one arm?

57. At a throw-in, a player must keep one foot on the ground. Correct?

58. At a penalty-kick, what should the referee order if a player from the defending side goes into the penalty area before the kick is taken?

59. A referee awards a goal. Ten seconds after the restart, he realises that he should have given the scorer offside. Can he cancel the goal?

60. A player scores a goal with the last kick of the first half. During half-time, the linesman tells the referee that the scorer handled the ball. Can he disallow the goal?

61. A team arrives for a cup-tie with only six players. Should the referee allow the match to start?

62. If he were strong enough, would a goalkeeper be allowed to throw the ball from his own penalty area into his opponents' goal and score?

63. Can a goal be scored direct from a corner-kick?

64. What decision does the referee give if the ball hits the corner-flag and rebounds into play?

65. Are square goal-posts allowed?

66. When a player has left the field of play to receive treatment, does he have to wait for play to stop before he can come back on?

67. Can a player who has been sent off to remove dangerous equipment be allowed back onto the field while play is in progress?

68. What signal does the referee use to indicate an indirect free-kick?

69. What signal does a linesman use to indicate a substitution is required?

70. Can a substitution be made while the match is in progress?

71. Can a substitute come onto the pitch from behind the goal?

72. How near to the ball can the defending players approach at the taking of a corner-kick?

73. Can a goalkeeper take a penalty-kick?

74. Who decides how much injury-time should be played?

75. What is the maximum weight of the ball?

76. Can a linesman award a free-kick?

77. Do the laws insist on goal nets?

78. Should a player be given offside whenever he is in an offside position?

79. There is nothing in the laws to stop football being played on ice. True or false?

80. When is the ball out of play?

81. At a dropped ball, the referee should insist on at least one player from each side being present. True or false?

82. If a player commits two offences of a different nature at the same time, which offence should the referee penalise?

83. Does a linesman have to bring his own flag when he goes to a match?

84. Can a celebrity ''kick-off'' who is not taking part in the game itself?

85. What action should the referee take if two players of the same team exchange blows within the field of play and while the ball is in play?

86. Can a player climb onto the shoulders of a team mate in order to attempt to head the ball?

87. If a player is guilty of misconduct during the half-time interval, should the referee take action?

88. If the captain of a team sees one of his own players commit an act of serious misconduct, can he order him from the field?

89. A team starts a match with three players missing. Two arrive during the first half, and the third, ten minutes before the end. Should they be permitted to take part in the match?

90. Can a player take part in a competitive match wearing glasses?

91. If a player is injured during the pre-match "kick-about", can he be replaced by another player?

92. When does the authority of the referee commence?

93. A team walks off the field in protest against a referee's decision. After a few minutes in the dressing room the team decides to return to the field. Should the referee then restart the match?

94. What would be the referee's decision if the ball were played backwards from the kick-off?

95. If the floodlights should fail, is there a maximum period of time that a match can be suspended while repairs are carried out?

96. If a referee signals a goal in anticipation that the ball is going to cross the goal-line but it does not do so, should the goal be allowed to stand?

97. How should the game be restarted when a player kicks the ball from an indirect free-kick directly into his opponents' goal?

98. Can a player taking a penalty-kick pass the ball backwards for a team mate to run onto and score?

99. What is the referee's decision if, from a throw-in, a player throws the ball directly into his own goal?

100. Is it possible for a player to be offside at the taking of a corner-kick?

CHAPTER TEN : STRANGE BUT TRUE

Two players follow the ball closely during the F.A. Cup Final in 1987. They both scored. Who are they?

1. Which England player (with twenty-five caps) actually made his international debut *against* England?

2. Who played in ordinary shoes instead of football boots and yet only failed to score in two of his thirteen England appearances?

3. When did Britain's Olympic football team, comprised solely of amateurs, beat the Bulgarian World Cup side?

4. Which club provided all eleven players for the England team?

5. Sheffield Wednesday's match with Aston Villa in 1898 took four months to complete. How come?

6. In which year was a Scottish international match at Hampden Park abandoned through rough play?

7. What was the minimum charge to watch a Football League match in 1960?

8. Who played in a Football League match when he was fifty-two years old?

9. Who played in an F.A. Cup Final when he was forty-one years old?

10. How old was Pelé when he made his Brazil debut?

11. Who appeared in over four hundred consecutive League matches for Tranmere Rovers?

12. Who played in all four Divisions of the League inside one year?

13. The great Di Stefano played for three different countries. Which were they?

14. Which club won a Scottish F.A. Cup tie 36-0 when some of the opposing team played in ordinary clothes.

15. What nationality were the railway workers who reputedly started football in Argentina?

16. What is the record crowd for an amateur match in England?

17. What is the smallest crowd ever to watch a Football League match?

18. Who were the opponents when 90,000 watched a Friendly at Chelsea?

19. Charlton Athletic and Derby County met twice in five days in 1946, once in the League and once in the F.A. Cup Final. What strange event occurred in both games?

20. Which Scottish League club plays in England?

21. Which country has played in sixteen matches in the World Cup Finals but never won?

22. The England World Cup team once played in the F.A. Charity Shield. True or false?

23. What was remarkable about Dennis Murray's goalkeeping debut for Crewe Alexandra?

24. Which club scored twenty-six goals in an F.A. Cup tie when the referee is reputed to have let the match go on thirty minutes too long?

25. Which country played twenty-nine Internationals between 1950 and 1954 and never lost?

26. Which foreign club side were undefeated in home league games for eight years?

27. Which club won the Football League Championship without losing a match and the F.A. Cup without conceding a goal in the same season?

28. In which year did the weather cause twenty-nine out of the thirty-two F.A. Cup third round ties to be postponed?

29   In which country was Eusebio, Portugal's greatest International, born?

30. Which father and son were inside-forwards in the same Stockport County line-up in 1951?

31. Burnley were fined for fielding ten reserves in a Football League match against Chelsea. What was the score?

32. What was the special significance of Southampton's home Football Combination fixture against Tottenham in 1951?

33. Which two clubs have won both the F.A. Cup and the F.A. Amateur Cup?

34. When was the first year in which all ninety-two Football League clubs entered the League Cup?

35. Who was the German goalkeeper who was the Football League's 'Player of the Year' in 1956?

36. The Chinese Cheung Chi Doy played for which Football League club in the 1960s?

37. The 1967 F.A. Charity Shield fixture between Manchester United and Tottenham is remembered for a bizarre goal. Who scored it?

38. 'Dixie' Dean registered sixty League goals in his record-breaking season, but how many did he score in that season in all competitions?

39. Who was the top goalscorer in the First Division in six different seasons?

40. Who was the Second Division's top goalscorer in three successive seasons from 1957 to 1960?

41. Which full-back scored ten goals for Liverpool in Season 1969-70, a total which included no penalties?

42. Who was the Arsenal player of the 1950s who once kicked the ball into his net when he (wrongly) thought that the referee had blown for time?

43. Which First Division full-back scored an own goal inside the first minute on two consecutive Saturdays in 1972?

44. All five Everton forwards scored inside eighteen minutes of a League match in 1931. Who were their opponents?

45. Which club won 10-0 at home in the League on the day before the Second World War started?

46. On which two Football League grounds did Northern Ireland play World Cup qualifying matches in 1973?

47. What is the connection between the Shah of Persia and one of the F.A.'s competitions?

48. Real Madrid star Raymond Kopa was voted 'European Footballer of the Year' in 1958. What was his real surname?

49. Who was Manager or General Manager of the same First Division club from 1945 to 1971?

50. In the 1974 World Cup one country did not lose a match and did not concede any goals, but they did not win the Cup. Who were they?

51. Pelé's former club, Santos, once drew a match 3-3 that had lasted three and a half hours. Who were their opponents?

52. Which ex-England striker once scored thirteen penalties in a season for his club?

53. How many Chelsea players finished the Football League match at Blackpool in 1932?

54. Which club finished their Italian First Division season with 'minus 10 points' in 1960?

55. Which monarch banned football in England because he wanted more time devoted to archery practice?

56. Which King in Eastern Europe chose his country's World Cup squad?

57. Has there ever been a Scottish League Division Three?

58. Which Football Legue club had a team consisting solely of Scotsmen?

59. Which present Football League club is reputed to have been largely instrumental in the forming of the Southern League in 1894?

60. Which bespectacled Belgian inside-forward won the last of his sixty-seven caps in 1967?

61. Which teams were involved when the first professional competitive match was played on a Sunday?

62. What was the first televised match after the last war?

63. How were 105,000 people able to watch Everton's Cup tie with Liverpool in 1967?

64. Who was the long throw specialist in the 1960s who could manage forty yards?

65. What limit on signing-on fees did the F.A. want to impose in 1898?

66. Who was the Exeter City trainer who had to play in the League match against Norwich because they were a man short?

67. Who played for both sides in the same League match?

68. What was the original name of the competition now called the U.E.F.A. Cup?

69. What weekly wage did the first professionals at Stoke City receive?

70. At the turn of the century what was the fee for playing for England?

71. Have Football League matches ever been played at Wembley Stadium, not counting play-offs?

72. Who scored seventy goals for England and Great Britain?

73. Which country walked off in protest during the 1920 Olympic Final?

74. Since the last war only two countries from outside Eastern Europe have won the Olympic soccer gold. Who are they?

75. The European Cup Winners' Cup Final of 1974 was watched by only 5,000. Which teams were playing?

76. Which League club went through a season winning every home match?

77. How many First Division matches did Tottenham win (out of forty-two) when they achieved the 'double' of the Season 1960-61?

78. Which Scottish club went through a season failing to win a single League game?

79. Who registered six 'hat-tricks' in the First Division in Season 1960-61?

80. Which club drew twenty-three League matches during Season 1978-79?

81. Which club played in twenty-five consecutive rounds of the Football League Cup, spread over five years, without losing a tie?

82. Who was the Reading goalkeeper who kept a clean sheet for 1,103 minutes in 1979?

83. Which clubs were involved when five penalties were awarded during a Second Division match in Season 1988-89?

84. The same player is the youngest scorer in an F.A. Cup Final and in a Football League Cup Final. Who is this?

85. Who played against England when he was forty-five years old?

86. Which Wrexham player was sent off only twenty seconds into a League match at Hull?

87. Who was the Brazilian who scored even more goals than Pelé?

88. Which country's team had to be persuaded to leave their hotel to play a World Cup qualifier and then lost 13-0?

89. Which club won the F.A. Youth Cup in each of the first five seasons of the competition?

90. Which Fourth Division team had 81,000 at one of their matches in 1988?

91. Crystal Palace won their F.A. Cup semi-final against Liverpool in 1990 to qualify for their first Wembley Final. But in the previous fourteen months Palace had twice been within ninety minutes of Wembley. Which were the two teams which had caused them disappointment?

92. Which European country's Cup Final finished: HB 1 NSI 0?

93. Which South American country has an 'Everton' and a 'Rangers' in their First Division?

94. What is the goalscoring feat attributed to the Frenchman, Stephan Stanis?

95. Who were the home club when eighty people watched a Scottish League match in 1979?

96. How many times has there been an 8-5 scoreline in a Football League match?

97. Which country has six grounds with a capacity of at least 100,000?

98. Who were 2-0 up after two minutes of a League match in 1956?

99. Which club was re-elected four times before going on to Division One and Wembley Cup Final success?

100. Italy won the World Cup in 1982 but could only draw with an African team in the first round. Which team was this?

ANSWERS

CHAPTER ONE – PLAYERS

1. John Barnes

2. He failed a drug test.

3. Alf Common (Sunderland to Middlesbrough, 1905)

4. Paul Allen (West Ham United, 1980)

5. None

6. It helped him to score against England ('The Hand of God').

7. Werder Bremen

8. Each of four transfers involved moving to a different country.

9. Eusebio (Portugal)

10. Bob Latchford

11. 'Dixie' Dean (60)

12. Stan Mortensen (Blackpool, 1953)

13. Patrick Battiston (France)

14. Bryan Robson (v France, 1982, 27 seconds)

15. Argentina, Colombia and Spain

16. Bobby Charlton

17. Joey Jones

18. 105

19. Derek Dooley

20. Jimmy McGrory

21. Bernard Joy

22. Frank Haffey

23. Most goals by an individual in a Scottish Cup tie (13)

24. Neil McBain (52)

25. He became the first substitute to score in the Football League.

26. Denis Law (Torino to Manchester United, 1962)

27. They have all played for and managed the League champions.

28. He was their goalkeeper.

29. The fastest own goal in a Football League match (6 seconds)

30. Chris Nicholl (Villa) scored all four goals.

31. West Bromwich Albion, Fulham, Leicester City and Shrewsbury Town

32. 66

33. Just Fontaine (France, 13 in 1958 tournament)

34. Ronnie Allen

35. Johnny Carey

36. Denis Law, for Manchester City in an abandoned tie at Luton in 1961

37. None

38. It caused his former club, Manchester United, to be relegated.

39. They also had Peter Shilton on their books.

40. Peter Shilton, Ray Clemence and Joe Corrigan

41. Alan Kennedy

42. Sampdoria

43. Kenny Dalglish

44. Newcastle United

45. Mike Kelly

46. John Aldridge (Liverpool, 1988)

47. George Mutch (Preston North End, 1938)

48. Edward and George Robledo

49. Kerry Davis

50. Johnny Haynes

51. Nat Lofthouse

52. Matthew Le Tissier

53. Trevor Booking

54. Lee Chapman, Gary Parker and Tony Cottee

55. Colin Harrison (467)

56. Don Givens (26 for Eire)

57. Clive Allen

58. Johan Neeskens and Paul Breitner

59. Vancouver Whitecaps

60. David Icke

61. Jamaica

62. Leicester City

63. Phil Neale played for Lincoln City.

64. Bill Slater (Blackpool)

65. Ron and Peter Springett

66. Terry Butcher

67. Romeo Zondervan

68. Eddie Firmani

69. Bolton Wanderers, Birmingham City, Blackburn Rovers and Bury

70. Grimsby Town and Lincoln City

71. John Osborne

72. Bert Trautmann

73. Clive Clark (West Bromwich Albion, 1967)

74. AC Milan

75. Cardiff City

76. The first goal scored in an F.A. Cup Final (for Wanderers, 1872)

77. Antonio Rattin

78. George Eastham (Stoke City)

79. John Thomson

80. Gerd Müller

81. Ron Flowers

82. Jim Baxter, the Scottish international wing-half

83. Jimmy McGrory

84. Ipswich Town

85. Jim McCalliog

91. Kenny Sansom

86. Steve Foster

87. Kevin Moran (Manchester United, 1985)

88. Kevin Keegan and Billy Bremner

89. Bari

90. Neil Webb

92. They have all played for Everton and England

93. Mark Wright

94. Eire

95. Ivan Golac

96. Tony Adams

97. Viv Anderson

98. Terry Butcher

99. Chris Woods

100. West Ham United

CHAPTER TWO – THE CLUBS

1. Notts County

2. Lincoln City

3. Nottingham Forest

4. Aston Villa

5. Birmingham City

6. Norwich City

7. Manchester City

8. Southampton

9. Newcastle United

10. Queens Park Rangers

11. Chelsea, Ipswich Town, Nottingham Forest, Sheffield United and West Bromwich Albion

12. Mansfield Town

13. Queens Park Rangers

14. West Ham United

15. Stoke City and Port Vale

16. Peterborough United

17. Liverpool

18. Preston North End

19. Chelsea

20. Darwen

21. Grimsby Town

22. Chester

23. Hull City

24. Coventry City

25. Scunthorpe United

26. Oxford United

27. Tottenham Hotspur and Nottingham Forest

28. Everton

29. Huddersfield Town, Arsenal and Liverpool

30. Brentford

31. Bristol Rovers

32. Arsenal

33. Everton

34. True.

35. Aston Villa (128 in 1930-31)

36. Stoke City (24 in 1984-85)

37. Liverpool (16 in 1978-79)

38. Plymouth Argyle

39. Sunderland

40. Arsenal

41. Nottingham Forest (42 matches)

42. Luton Town

43. Leyton Orient

44. Wolverhampton Wanderers

45. Charlton Athletic and Port Vale

46. Sheffield United

47. Crystal Palace

48. Swansea Town

49. West Bromwich Albion (1931)

50. None

51. Tom Finney

52. Blackpool

53. Derby County

54. Tottenham Hotspur (31 in 1960-61)

55. Nottingham Forest

56. Birmingham City

57. Scarborough

58. Wolverhampton Wanderers

59. Liverpool (18)

60. Preston North End (1888-89)

61. Ipswich Town

62. Swindon Town

63. Oldham Athletic

64. Arsenal

65. Norwich City (23 in 1978-79)

66. False

67. Manchester City (1957-58)

68. Silver grey

69. Arsenal

70. Manchester United

71. Wimbledon

72. Newcastle United and Exeter City

73. Bobby Charlton

74. Chelsea

75. True

76. White Hart Lane

77. True

78. Southend United

79. Colin Bell

80. Chester

81. True

82. Peter Shilton

83. Plymouth Argyle

84. Luton Town

85. Ipswich Town

86. Sheffield Wednesday

87. Twice

88. Peter Shilton

89. Everton's

90. West Ham United

91. Arsenal

92. Lincoln City

93. Tranmere Rovers

94. Tottenham Hotspur

95. Watford

96. Scunthorpe United

97. Emlyn Hughes

98. West Ham United

99. Highbury

100. Arsenal's

CHAPTER THREE – MANAGERS

1. Joe Mercer

2. Herbert Chapman

3. Norwich City, Manchester City and Aston Villa

4. Brian Clough

5. Dave Bassett

6. Dave Mackay, George Graham and Kenny Dalglish

7. Sheffield Wednesday

8. Jock Stein

9. Bertie Mee

10. Dino Zoff

11. The 'academy' at West Ham United

12. Cesar Menotti

13. Barcelona

14. Bill Shankly

15. West Bromwich Albion

16. Tommy Docherty

17. Ossie Ardiles (Swindon Town) and Danny Bergara (Stockport County)

18. Cheri Lunghi

19. 0-0 (v Portugal, 1974)

20. Allan Brown

21. 2

22. Sporting Lisbon

23. John Docherty

24. Hartlepool United

25. Bob Paisley

26. Malcolm Allison

27. Real Sociedad and Real Madrid

28. Gary Lineker, Mark Hughes and Steve Archibald

29. Charles Hughes

30. 6

31. Matt Busby

32. Azeglio Vicini

33. Sepp Piontek

34. Birmingham City

35. Jim Smith

36. Fulham and Vancouver Whitecaps

37. Johnny Giles

38. Brian Clough (for Trevor Francis)

39. Matt Busby

40. Jimmy Hill

41. Mike England

42. Terry Neill

43. Charlton Athletic

44. Birmingham City

45. Both have played at wing-half for the club.

46. Ted Bates

47. Director

48. Barnsley

49. Willie Ormond

50. Alec Stock was in Yeovil's team when they knocked Sunderland out of the F.A. Cup in 1949.

51. He took Second Division Fulham to the 1975 F.A. Cup Final.

52. Yes (Port Vale)

53. Alf Ramsey

54. 1977

55. Keith Burkinshaw

56. Johan Cruyff

57. Malcolm Allison

58. Helmut Schoen

59. Preston North End, Wigan Athletic (as caretaker)

60. Athletic Bilbao

61. Rinus Michels

62. George Curtis and John Sillett

63. Phil Neal (Bolton Wanderers)

64. Berti Vogts

65. Yes

66. Terry Venables

67. Don Revie

68. Billy Bonds

69. He wore 'lucky' white spats.

70. Danny Blanchflower

71. Bob Stokoe

72. Terry Venables

73. Malcolm Allison

74. Alf Ramsey

75. F.A. Cup, Football League Cup, European Cup Winners' Cup and U.E.F.A. Cup

76. Stan Cullis

77. Joe Fagan

78. Ian Greaves (Mansfield Town)

79. Malcolm MacDonald (Fulham)

80. Thirteen days (J.Cochrane, Reading)

81. Ian Bowyer

82. Terry Cooper

83. Steve Coppell

84. Alex Ferguson (Scotland) and Josef Venglos (Czechoslovakia)

85. Darlington, Torquay United and Hartlepool United

86. Mick Mills

87. Howard Wilkinson

88. Phil Taylor

89. Paynter, Fenton, Greenwood, Lyall, Macari and Bonds

90. Southampton

91. Millwall

92. Bobby Ferguson

93. Mike Keen

94. Peter Shilton

95. Ted Drake, Ken Shellito, Geoff Hurst and John Hollins

96. Tim Ward

97. Yes

98. John Cartwright

99. Tony Waiters

100. Terry Neill

CHAPTER FOUR – NON-LEAGUE

1. Wealdstone
2. Alan Smith
3. England
4. 32,000
5. South Liverpool
6. Runcorn
7. Bishop's Stortford
8. A team of Oxbridge Students that twice won the F.A. Amateur Cup
9. 1960
10. Skelmersdale United
11. 1984
12. 1949
13. Peter Taylor
14. Hoddesdon Town
15. Peter Swan
16. Bashley
17. Ian Moores
18. Vale Recreation
19. Nottingham Forest
20. Barton Rovers
21. Stamford
22. Altrincham

23. Lincoln City and Wycombe Wanderers

24. Weymouth

25. Mark Ward

26. Lincoln City

27. Altrincham

28. Altrincham

29. Aylesbury United

30. Their first match in August was postponed because of the weather.

31. Barnsley

32. Macclesfield Town

33. Newport County

34. Rod Haider

35. Bishop's Stortford

36. Southall

37. Scotland

38. Wembley Stadium

39. John Faulkner

40. Telford United

41. 10

42. Weymouth

43. Macclesfield Town

44. True (Manchester United away, F.A. Cup, 1949)

45. Crystal Palace F.C.

46. AFC Bournemouth

47. Farnborough Town

48. Harrow Borough

49. Ted Croker

50. Marlow

51. Slough Town

52. Alex Stepney

53. Chesham United

54. Leicester City FC

55. Oxford City

56. Walton & Hersham (Brighton away, F.A. Cup, 1973)

57. Yes

58. Banstead Athletic

59. Eastbourne United

60. Cyrille Regis

61. Purfleet

62. Canvey Island

63. Redhill

64. Steyning Town

65. Merthyr Tydfil

66. Southern League

67. Bath City, Dartford and Macclesfield Town

68. Cambridge City

69. Dorchester Town

70. Fareham Town

71. Stroud

72. Halesowen Town

73. Lee Smelt

74. Margate

75. Falmouth Town

76. Halesowen Town

77. Hounslow Town

78. 2 (AFC Bournemouth and Bournemouth Poppies)

79. Colin Cowperthwaite

80. Goole Town

81. An artificial pitch

82. Wycombe Wanderers

83. A Nigerian XI

84. Jimmy Case and John Aldridge

85. Northwich Victoria and Witton Albion

86. Sutton United, Sutton Town and Sutton Coldfield Town

87. Warrington Town

88. Hallam

89. Bishop Auckland

90. Dorking

91. Redhill

92. 26,000

93. Wrexham (at Newcastle United F.C.)

94. Kingstonian

95. None
96. Douglas High School O.B.
97. Corinthian-Casuals
98. Southern Amateur League
99. Old Boys League
100. Ian Crawley

CHAPTER FIVE – F.A. CUP

1. 1923
2. It was stolen and never recovered.
3. Yes (Cardiff City, 1927)
4. John Aldridge
5. Tottenham Hotspur
6. Yes
7. Altrincham and Sutton United
8. A curse thought to have caused injury to players in the Finals (particularly the 1950s).
9. Paul Allen
10. He played in nine Finals.
11. Bill Shankly
12. No
13. Ricky Villa
14. 15
15. Charlton Athletic (1946)
16. He wore glasses.
17. Ted MacDougall (Bournemouth)
18. Denis Law
19. True
20. Alvechurch v Oxford City (1971)
21. Walthamstow Avenue
22. 8

23. 8

24. Yes (Ipswich Town, 1978)

25. Chelsea v Leeds United (1970)

26. Wanderers

27. Bill Slater (Blackpool, 1951)

28. Wimbledon

29. Trevor Brooking

30. 1946 and 1947

31. Dave Mackay

32. To play in the F.A. Charity Shield

33. Corinthians

34. Norman Whiteside (Manchester United, 1983, 18 years 18 days)

35. David Nish (Leicester City, 1969, 21 years 212 days)

36. True (Bradford City v Norwich City at Lincoln, 1915)

37. 1930

38. 1901

39. Newcastle United

40. 1915

41. 6-0 (Bury v Derby County, 1903)

42. No

43. False

44. 1970

45. No one

46. Yes (1933)

47. Nat Lofthouse (Bolton Wanderers)

48. True

49. Tottenham Hotspur, Arsenal and Liverpool

50. 5

51. Bedford Town

52. Barnet

53. Sunderland

54. Five

55. Youngest player in a Cup tie (15 years 88 days)

56. Fifty guineas

57. Tottenham Hotspur

58. Wimbledon

59. 13

60. 1927

61. The holders were given a bye to the Final and were challenged by the club which had won through the earlier rounds.

62. True

63. The penalty-kick was not introduced into football until 1891.

64. Charlton Athletic (1946)

65. Pat Jennings (Arsenal)

66. Portsmouth

67. 1914 (King George V)

68. Dick Pym

69. Yes (1937, 1938)

70. Wolves (1939)

71. They scored for both sides in the Final

72. True

73. 1967 (Tottenham Hotspur v Chelsea)

74. £25

75. 1912

76. Kennington Oval

77. No

78. Oxford United (1964)

79. True

80. Notts County (1894)

81. In all six rounds, including the Final, they had faced First Division opposition.

82. Manchester United

83. Joe Smith

84. Joe Hulme

85. False

86. West Bromwich Albion (1888)

87. Port Vale

88. False

89. Close to the present West Brompton Underground Station in S.W. London

90. 1966

91. Dave Mackay

92. Jimmy Case

93. Everton

94. 1984

95. Mark Wright

96. They had not lost in the 120 matches in which Rush had scored.

97. Sutton United

98. 109

99. No

100. The losing team's ribbons on the Cup

CHAPTER SIX – ENGLAND

1. 18
2. Bernard Joy
3. Billy Wright
4. Joe Baker (Hibernian)
5. Argentinian captain Rattin was sent off but refused to go.
6. Republic of Ireland
7. Alf Ramsey and Bobby Robson
8. Joe Mercer
9. 100,000
10. Brazil
11. Australia
12. Billy Wright
13. Bobby Charlton
14. Denis Compton
15. Charltons (Jack and Bobby)/Formans (Frank and Frederick)
16. Cloughs (Nigel and Brian)/Easthams (both George)
17. 1955
18. Lancaster Gate
19. Malcolm MacDonald
20. Bobby Charlton
21. Arsenal
22. 4-3

23. Scotland
24. Charles Alcock
25. Austria
26. Yugoslavia
27. Neil Webb
28. Stanley Matthews
29. Bobby Moore
30. 10
31. Alan Mullery
32. 1
33. 1950
34. 2
35. James Mullen
36. Scotland
37. Scotland
38. Luther Blissett
39. Gary Bailey
40. Peter Bonetti
41. Steve Bull
42. Terry Butcher
43. Peter Davenport
44. Paul Goddard and Steve Perryman
45. Portsmouth
46. 1979

47. Glenn Hoddle

48. Wales

49. Gary Lineker

50. Brian Little

51. Nat Lofthouse

52. Phil Neal

53. Mick Mills

54. Martin Peters

55. 6

56. 20

57. Tony Waiters

58. Paraguay

59. Belgium

60. France, Mexico and Uruguay

61. Brazil, Italy and 'Team America'

62. All sky blue

63. Away to Denmark in September 1982

64. 1970

65. Larry Gaetjens

66. Yes

67. Ireland

68. Against Brazil in 1990

69. Kevin Hector

70. Tommy Wright

71. Malta

72. 1972

73. Morocco

74. Peter Beardsley

75. U.S.A.

76. 1961

77. Bill Nicholson's against Portugal in 1951 (19 seconds)

78. Gary Lineker

79. South Korea

80. U.S.S.R.

81. Bryan Robson

82. Brazil, Uruguay and Chile

83. Yes

84. Ron Flowers

85. Alf Ramsey

86. Jimmy Greaves/Terry Paine

87. Danny Wallace

88. Joe Royle

89. Peter Taylor

90. 11

91. Scotland

92. Hungary

93. Phil Parkes

94. Goodison Park

95. 1-0 to England
96. Against Canada
97. 'Dixie' Dean
98. 1989
99. Steve Bloomer
100. Butcher in Singapore/Barnes in Jamaica

CHAPTER SEVEN – EUROPEAN

1. Real Madrid
2. 4
3. Juventus
4. Liam Brady
5. Manchester United (1968)
6. Tottenham Hotspur (1963)
7. U.S.S.R.
8. Juventus
9. 2
10. Paris St. Germain
11. Liverpool (1977)
12. Benfica
13. Barcelona
14. Castilla
15. Guus Hiddink
16. France
17. Real Sociedad and Real Madrid
18. Seville
19. Barcelona and Bayern Munich
20. Rome
21. Liverpool (1984)
22. Yes (1976)
23. AC Milan

24. Arthur Ellis (England)

25. Nottingham Forest

26. Real Sociedad

27. Fiorentina

28. Emilio Butragueno

29. Hampden Park, Glasgow

30. Manchester United

31. Juventus

32. No

33. True (Celtic, 1967)

34. AZ Alkmaar

35. Linfield

36. Tottenham Hotspur

37. Maradona's club Napoli is sponsored by Mars.

38. Albania

39. Yes (Fairs Cup)

40. Santiago Bernabeu Stadium

41. Stanley Matthews

42. Bordeaux

43. Belgium

44. False

45. Bayern Munich and Real Madrid

46. Bobby Charlton

47. Ipswich Town and Leeds United

48. Rotterdam

49. 3

50. Español

51. Sergei Baltacha

52. Pisa

53. Cagliari

54. Spain

55. AC Milan

56. Real Madrid

57. Notts County

58. Nantes

59. Sweden

60. Marseille

61. Brehme, Matthäus and Klinsmann

62. Atletico Madrid

63. Real Madrid

64. Arthur Ellis (England)

65. 21-0 to Chelsea

66. 1984

67. Peter Lorimer

68. Third place (1968)

69. 135,000 (1960)

70. Frans Thijssen and Arnold Muhren

71. Belgium

72. True

73. Champion Clubs' Cup

74. Hungary

75. Barcelona

76. Rovaniemi

77. Yes (1961)

78. Chelsea

79. True (Kazimierz Deyna)

80. Trevor Francis

81. Bobby Moncur

82. Manchester United and Aston Villa

83. Brondby

84. San Marino and Faroe Islands

85. All blue

86. Merthyr Tydfil

87. Alan Sealey

88. Panathinaikos

89. Red Star

90. Udinese

91. Italy

92. Real Madrid

93. Swansea Town (1961)

94. U.E.F.A. Cup

95. Hamburg

96. PSV Eindhoven

97. United

98. David Fairclough

99. Yes (Champion Clubs' Cup, 1963)

100. Mitropa Cup

CHAPTER EIGHT – WORLD CUP

1. True (1930)
2. Gerd Müller (10)
3. Uruguay
4. Roberto Rojas
5. Brazil
6. Daniel Passarella
7. Enzo Bearzot
8. Cameroon and England
9. Italy
10. Uruguay
11. 1970
12. Mexico and Italy
13. Martin Peters
14. Gary Lineker
15. 1970
16. 1950
17. Peter Bonetti
18. Gary Lineker (6)
19. David O'Leary
20. Antonio Rattin (Argentina)
21. 3
22. 1958

23. Antonio Cabrini (Italy)

24. USA

25. Brazil

26. Bobby Charlton

27. 1958

28. Italy

29. Mario Kempes (6)

30. 12

31. Ron Springett and Peter Bonetti

32. Bobby Robson

33. Kenneth Wolstenholme, the TV commentator

34. No

35. Gerd Müller (14)

36. Jules Rimet, President of F.I.F.A. 1920-54

37. France, Yugoslavia, Romania and Belgium

38. Hungary (v El Salvador, 1982)

39. One (1990)

40. H.M. The Queen

41. Lothar Matthäus

42. 1958

43. White City Stadium

44. 4

45. Mick Mills

46. Italy

47. Larry Gaetjens

48. No

49. Wolfgang Weber

50. England

51. East Germany

52. Pedro Monzon (Argentina, 1990)

53. Antonio Carbajal

54. Louis Laurent (France)

55. Salvio Gazzaniga

56. 6

57. 'Toto' Schillaci (6)

58. 4

59. Alex Ferguson

60. 1978

61. Stuart Pearce and Chris Waddle

62. Holland

63. Eusebio (9)

64. Jairzinho

65. Diego Maradona

66. 3

67. Ally McLeod

68. Andreas Brehme

69. True

70. 2

71. Omam Biyik

72. George Courtney

73. Woods, Seaman, Hodge and Beasant

74. Roger Milla (Cameroon)

75. Yugoslavia

76. Portugal

77. Italy

78. 2

79. 19

80. Zaire

81. U.S.A. and Germany

82. Peter Shilton

83. Billy Bingham

84. Emilio Butragueno (Spain)

85. Rob Rensenbrink

86. Carlos Alberto

87. Vittorio Pozzo (Italy)

88. Robson, Shilton and Butcher

89. Luton

90. No

91. Osvaldo Ardiles

92. Osvaldo Ardiles

93. Peter Shilton

94. No

CHAPTER NINE – LAWS OF THE GAME

1. No

2. A penalty-kick

3. Choice of ends or the kick-off

4. No. Players have a right to an interval at half-time.

5. To award a goal

6. No. Time is extended to allow a penalty-kick to be taken.

7. Yes

8. No

9. Yes, in the sense that the line forms part of the penalty area.

10. A kick at the ball while it is stationary on the ground in the centre of the field of play.

11. On their own goal-line

12. Not necessarily. In international matches, for example, the referee wears a strip the colour of which is distinctive from the colours worn by the competing teams.

13. No

14. The throw-in is taken by a player of the opposing team.

15. Only if foul or abusive language is used; otherwise the player is cautioned.

16. Boots are normally worn, although the laws refer only to 'footwear'.

17. A player could have been 'sent-off' if his equipment had not conformed to the laws.

18. The game is resumed by an indirect free-kick awarded to the opposing team from the place where the offence occurred.

19. (a) yellow, (b) red

20. No. A goal cannot be allowed if the ball has been prevented by some outside agent from passing over the goal-line.

21 No. The taker cannot play the ball a second time until it has been touched or played by another player.

22. That a player could not be offside if two (instead of three) opponents were nearer their own goal-line when the ball was last played

23. The International F.A. Board

24. No

25. No

26. 4

27. Yes

28. 44 yards

29. Yes. In the case of improper conduct a referee may dispense with a linesman's services and arrange for a substitute to be appointed.

30. A direct free-kick awarded to the opposing team

31. To mark an area into which no player, other than the taker, can go while a penalty-kick is being taken

32. It must be not more than 28 inches and not less than 27 inches.

33. No

34. (a) caution the player, then (b) send the player off

35. Stanley Rous

36. The goal consists of two upright posts which are eight yards apart, joined by a horizontal crossbar the lower edge of which is eight feet from the ground.

37. (c)

38. No. Flags at the half-way line are not obligatory.

39. Yes, if the referee feels that it may constitute a danger to other players.

40. No

41. No, because the ball has not travelled the distance of its own circumference and is therefore not yet in play.

42. 5 feet

43. No. The kick may be taken from any point within that half of the goal area in which the offence occurred.

44. 17

45. Law Eleven

46. No

47. No

48. No

49. 120 yards

50. 2

51. Kicking (an opponent), tripping, jumping (at an opponent), charging violently, charging from behind, striking or spitting, holding, pushing and handball

52. No. A goal can only be scored against the offending team.

53. No exact time is stipulated. It is up to the referee to decide if the goalkeeper is guilty of timewasting.

54. Jersey or shirt, shorts, stockings, shinguards and footwear

55. 10 yards

56. No

57. No. Part of each foot must be on the ground.

58. The referee shall allow the kick to proceed, if he has signalled for it to be taken. The kick is retaken, if a goal has not been scored.

59. No

60. No

61. The International FA Board's view is that a match should not be considered valid if either team has fewer than seven players.

62. Yes

63. Yes

64. Play is allowed to continue.

65. Yes

66. No, but he must wait for the referee's signal of

acknowledgement.

67. No. The player may only re-enter the game at a moment when the ball has ceased to be in play.

68. He raises an arm above his head.

69. He holds his flag in a horizontal position above the head.

70. No. He can only enter the field during a stoppage in the game.

71. No. He must enter at the half-way line.

72. 10 yards

73. Yes

74. The referee

75. 16 ounces

76. No

77. No

78. No, only if the player is (a) interfering with play or with an opponent, or (b) seeking to gain an advantage by being in that position.

79. True, but the referee always has the power to decide on the fitness of the playing surface.

80. (a) When it has wholly crossed the goal-line or touch-line, whether on the ground or in the air. (b) When

the game has been stopped by the referee.

81. False. The referee has no obligation to insist on any particular number of players being present.

82. The more serious offence

83. No. The linesmen should be equipped with flags by the club on whose ground the match is played.

84. No

85. Send the players off and restart the game with an indirect free-kick against the offending team.

86. No. An indirect free-kick should be awarded to the opposing team.

87. Yes. The referee's authority continues during the interval, both on the field and in the dressing rooms.

88. No. Only the referee can send a player off.

89. Yes. The number can be made up any time during the period of the match.

90. Yes, provided the referee does not consider them to be a danger to other players or to the player himself.

91. Yes

92. As soon as he enters the field of play

93. No. When a team leaves the field without permission, the referee has no option but to abandon the match.

94. To order the kick-off to be retaken

95. No. This would be at the referee's discretion.

96. No

97. With a goal-kick to the opposing team.

98. No. The ball must be kicked forward.

99. To award a corner-kick to the opposing team

100. No

CHAPTER TEN – STRANGE BUT TRUE

1. Stan Mortensen

2. Dr. Tinsley Lindley

3. 1971

4. Corinthians

5. The original game was abandoned after 79½ minutes and the remaining 10½ minutes were played later in the season

6. 1963 (v Austria)

7. 2/6d

8. Neil McBain (New Brighton)

9. Walter Hampson (Newcastle United)

10. 16

11. Harold Bell

12. Anthony McNamara

13. Argentina, Colombia and Spain

14. Arbroath

15. British

16. 100,000 (F.A. Amateur Cup Finals 1951-55)

17. 13 (Stockport County v Leicester City, Division 2, 1921)

18. Moscow Dynamo (1945)

19. The ball burst

20. Berwick Rangers

21. Bulgaria

22. True (1950-51)

23. He conceded 11 goals against Lincoln City in 1951.

24. Preston North End (v Hyde, 1887)

25. Hungary

26. Real Madrid

27. Preston North End

28. 1963

29. Mozambique

30. Alec and David Herd

31. 4-4

32. First competitive fixture in Britain played under lights

33. Old Carthusians and Wimbledon

34. 1969

35. Bert Trautmann

36. Blackpool

37. Pat Jennings

38. 82

39. Jimmy Greaves

40. Brian Clough

41. Chris Lawler

42. Dennis Evans

43. Tommy Wright

44. Charlton Athletic

45. Bournemouth

46. Coventry City's and Fulham's

47. He donated the F.A. Sunday Cup trophy.

48. Kopaszewski

49. Sir Matt Busby (Manchester United)

50. Belgium

51. Penarol

52. Francis Lee (Manchester City, 1971-72)

53. 6

54. Genoa

55. Edward III

56. King Carol of Romania

57. Yes (it was scrapped in 1955)

58. Accrington Stanley (1955-56)

59. Millwall

60. Josef Jurion

61. Wisbech and Dunstable (Southern League, 1967)

62. Barnet v Tooting

63. 40,000 watched on closed circuit television at Anfield.

64. Bobby Woodruff

65. £10

66. James Gallagher (1949)

67. James Oakes (Port Vale v Charlton Athletic, 1932-33)

68. The International Industries Fairs Inter-Cities Cup.

69. 2/6d

70. £1

71. Yes (Clapton Orient played two 'home' matches in 1930-31)

72. Vivian Woodward

73. Czechoslovakia

74. Sweden and France

75. Magdeburg and AC Milan

76. Brentford (Division Three (South), 1929-30)

77. 31

78. Vale of Leven (1891-92)

79. Jimmy Greaves

80. Norwich City

81. Liverpool

82. Steve Death

83. Crystal Palace and Brighton

84. Norman Whiteside

85. Billy Meredith (for Wales, 1920)

86. Ambrose Brown

87. Arthur Friedenreich (1910-30)

88. Fiji (v New Zealand, 1981)

89. Manchester United

90. Burnley (Sherpa Van Trophy Final)

91. Nottingham Forest and Chelsea (Simod Cup/Zenith Data Systems Cup)

92. Faroe Islands

93. Chile

94. Scored 16 for Racing Club Lens in a French Cup tie

95. Meadowbank Thistle

96. 3

97. Brazil

98. Ipswich Town (v Brentford, Division Three (South))

99. Norwich City

100. Cameroon

Picture Questions

Chapter 1. Mike Phelan

Chapter 2. David Burrows

Chapter 3. Franz Beckenbauer

Chapter 4. West Auckland

Chapter 5. George Curtis's

Chapter 6. Holland

Chapter 7. Eusebio

Chapter 8. Gordon Milne

Chapter 9. George Courtney

Chapter 10. Keith Houchen and Gary Mabbutt

Also available from Rosters,

The Official Liverpool Quiz Book
Patrick Whyte

More than 800 questions about one of the country's best loved teams. Designed by quiz master Patrick Whyte to provide hours of fun and discussion.

Available from bookshops or Liverpool F.C. club shop.
£2.95

The Millwall Quiz Book
Patrick Whyte

With over a hundred years of the clubs history to cover, Patrick Whyte has compiled a book which will test the Lions masterminds.

Available from bookshops or Millwall F.C. club shop.£2.95

The Official Derby County F.C. Quiz Book
Patrick Whyte

Ideal for all Rams fans. Packed with over 800 questions to test your knowledge of the club you support.

Available only from the Derby County F.C. club shop.
£3.95

No Fishcakes On Matchdays: The inside story of Crystal Palace's 1989-90 season
Deano Standing

From the euphoria on a mid-summer's day as Palace defeated Blackburn Rovers to clinch a place in the First Division through to sadness as the F.A. Cup slipped from their grasp. This is the remarkable story of the Eagles in what turned out to be the most successful season in the club's history. Deano Standing, who worked in the publications department, gives his inside view of those turbulent and emotional months as the fans faced defeat one week and victory the next.

"Wonderful read" BBC TV Network South-East, also recommended by LBC, Greater London Radio, Croydon Advertiser and South London Press.

Available from bookshops.   £4.95

Betting to Win
Luke Johnson and Hugh Osmond

If you know the odds and how to analyse form you can improve your chances of winning. Inside Luke Johnson and Hugh Osmond reveal:

* The correct odds for various types of gambling
* The psychology of betting
* How to detect cheats and hustlers
* The thinking behind popular betting systems
* How house percentages work

The guide includes advice on horse racing, card games, casino games, bingo, pools, dogs, slot machines and gambling with dice. The perfect companion to help you get on to a winning steak.

Available from bookshops. £5.95

If you have any difficulty in obtaining a copy of the book you require please send a cheque or postal order for the cost of the book plus £1 for postage and packing to Rosters, 23 Welbeck St, London W1M 7PG.